EVOLUTION ILLU
WATERF(

G000166243

EVOLUTION ILLUSTRATED BY WATERFOWL

DAVID LACK F.R.S.

ILLUSTRATIONS BY
ROBERT GILLMOR

BLACKWELL SCIENTIFIC PUBLICATIONS
OXFORD LONDON EDINBURGH MELBOURNE

© 1974 Blackwell Scientific Publications
Osney Mead, Oxford
3 Nottingham Street, London W1M 3RA
9 Forrest Road, Edinburgh
P.O. Box 9, North Balwyn, Victoria, Australia

ISBN 0 632 08130 9 Cloth
ISBN 0 632 08250 x Paper

First published 1974

Distributed in the United States of America by
Harper & Row, Publishers, Inc.
and in Canada by
J. B. Lippincott Company of Canada Ltd, Toronto

Printed and bound in Great Britain by
Hazell Watson & Viney Ltd,
Aylesbury

CONTENTS

1   The Problem   7

2   The Waterfowl Family   8

3   Principles of Classification   11

4   Practical Difficulties in Classification   13

5   The Naming of Species   16

6   The Generic Names   19

7   The Higher Taxonomic Groups   22

8   The Naming of Subspecies   25

9   The Nature of Subspecies   27

10   The Subspecies of Canada Goose   31

11   The Ducks of Remote Islands   34

12   The Transition from Subspecies to Species   38

13   Colour Phases   41

14   Domestic Breeds of Waterfowl   44

15   Hybrid Ducks   47

16   Specific Recognition Characters   50

17   Sexual Selection   54

18   Competition between Species   59

19   Adaptive Radiation   64

20   Convergent Evolution   68

21   Adaptations for Breeding   73

22   Moult and Movements   77

23   Conclusion   81

APPENDICES

1   List of Waterfowl   84

2   Glossary of Biological Terms   88

Index   94

1 · THE PROBLEM

In Britain, fifteen species of waterfowl breed regularly and a few more do so occasionally, while another twelve are regular and a few others are occasional in winter. They include swans, geese, dabbling ducks, freshwater diving ducks and sea ducks. A visit to a collection of living waterfowl, such as that at the Wildfowl Trust at Slimbridge, will show that many more kinds occur in other parts of the world, including whole groups not found in Britain, such as the whistling ducks and stifftails, and in all there are nearly 150 living species.

How did this diversity of forms come into existence, and why do they differ from each other? This problem is, in miniature, that of all animal life, and the waterfowl have been used in this booklet to show the main principles of animal classification and evolution. Why choose the waterfowl? First because, between them, they illustrate most of the important stages in the evolutionary process, and secondly because they can be seen alive at the Wildfowl Trust and other collections, so that the student need not rely for his examples on museum skins or bones. For the many who live too far from such collections to visit them, I hope that Robert Gillmor's illustrations will be a fine substitute.

Charles Darwin in his book *The Origin of Species*, published in 1859, solved two problems. He showed first, the *fact* of evolution, that the living species of animals have been derived by slow change from pre-existing animals. Secondly, he postulated the *means* of evolution, that it occurs by the 'natural selection' of small hereditary changes; far more animals are born than survive to breed, and some hereditary types (genotypes) are less well suited to the environment than others, so they survive less well and leave fewer offspring than others. Darwin did not consider a third question, namely why there are

7

many different kinds or species, clearly separated from each other, instead of a series of intergrading forms, and he did not discuss how new species might originate.

To help the reader, the biological terms used in this book are defined when first mentioned, and they have been defined again in a glossary, arranged alphabetically, in Appendix 2 (starting p. 88), preceded by Appendix 1 (starting p. 84), which gives a list of the waterfowl of the world.

2 · THE WATERFOWL FAMILY

The waterfowl are a group of birds so clear-cut that it is easy to tell which species belong to it and which do not. A few other swimming birds, such as cormorants and divers (or loons), resemble ducks superficially in some ways, but they are at once distinguished by close examination.

Typically, waterfowl have a flattened beak, with a distinct 'nail' at the tip, and though the beak differs in shape in different species, it is unlike that of other kinds of birds. The three main toes are webbed, and the short legs are usually placed far back on the body (Fig. 2), with the result that the birds swim well but walk clumsily. Nearly all of them fly strongly, with powerful and continuous wing-beats uninterrupted by glides, and they look characteristic in the air, their long necks and short tails making the wings appear to be near the back of the body. There is no need to mention their internal anatomy, except that the syrinx, the vocal apparatus, is elaborate and peculiar, and with it they utter their characteristic quacks, whistles or honks.

One important aspect of animal evolution cannot be demon-

FIGURE 1. Winter scene with a wide variety of waterfowl. From top to bottom: flying, Grey geese; Whooper swans, *Cygnus cygnus cygnus*; Wigeon, *Anas penelope*; Goosander, *Mergus merganser*; Smew, *M. albellus*; Pochard, *Aythya ferina*; Tufted duck, *Aythya fuligula*; Shoveler, *Anas clypaeta*; Pintail, *A. acuta*; Mallard, *A. platyrhynchos*; Teal, *A. crecca*.

strated by means of waterfowl, namely the past, since fossil remains are few and incomplete, as in other groups of birds. The living species are presumably the survivors of a much larger number; indeed fossil bones have been attributed to roughly 100 further extinct species. The earliest of these, of two distinctive (and extinct) types, come from the late Eocene period, which means that waterfowl were already in existence near the start of the Cenozoic (or Tertiary) era, around 50–100 million years ago. It is probably somewhat earlier than this that the waterfowl and most other groups of living birds diverged from each other, as did many groups of mammals.

FIGURE 2. Drake Goldeneye.

At the present day, waterfowl are found in all parts of the world where there is fresh water, while some species are marine and a few live on dry land. Most of them eat vegetable food, but some take molluscs, crustaceans or fish. While all of them are built on a similar plan, within it they show much diversity, particularly in the shape of their beaks. The smallest species are the tropical Cotton Teal or pygmy geese, which weigh 350 grams (¾ lb) or less. At the other extreme, the Trumpeter Swan (Fig. 3) is one of the heaviest birds that flies, its average weight being over 10 kg (with a maximum of 38 lb).

FIGURE 3. Trumpeter Swan *Cygnus cygnus buccinator* and Cotton Teal *Nettapus coromandelianus.*

3 · PRINCIPLES OF CLASSIFICATION

The principles of evolution could not be understood, or even formulated, until many different kinds of animals had been recognised, named, and arranged in groups. The first classification which we should call scientific, because related forms were grouped together, was that of the English naturalists Willughby and Ray in the 17th century. (Willughby died young and his *Ornithology* was improved and published after his death by his friend Ray, who was primarily a botanist.) Another big advance, this time in the naming of species, came with the invention of the binomial system (described later) by the Swedish naturalist Linnaeus in the 18th century. These were essential prior steps to the theory of evolution, put forward in the next century.

For the same reason, in this book the classification of the

waterfowl is considered before their evolution. The 150 living species are too many to be considered individually, so they are put in different groups. This process we already started as children, when we learned to call some of them 'geese', others 'swans', and so on. But when all the waterfowl of the world are considered, English vernacular names may become misleading, and it is better to use precise scientific names, particularly as these are international. The waterfowl, for instance, are termed the Anatidae (from *anas*, the Latin for a duck and *idae*, the Greek ending used to denote a family).

The basic aim of animal classification is to group together those species which are related to each other and to separate them from other groups. It therefore serves the same purpose as a library catalogue, in which books on the same subject are placed together, and are put near to books on different but related subjects. But there is an important difference between a catalogue of books and a classification of animals. The books can be arranged on one of several different plans, and so long as the librarian is consistent, each may be convenient. For instance, a book on the life of Charles Darwin might reasonably be placed by one librarian among the biographies, by another in the biology section, and by yet another among the histories of thought in the 19th century.

When it comes to animals, however, the aim is not merely to provide a convenient catalogue, but to show evolutionary relationships. For this, wide knowledge is needed, as it is not easy to distinguish superficial resemblances from true affinities. In the 16th century, for instance, bats were grouped with birds, but we now know that they are really mammals, because they have hair, not feathers, and give birth to young instead of laying eggs. Their resemblance to birds is superficial, due to their use of the front limbs for flying. As a more subtle example of the same kind of difficulty, the waterfowl formerly called 'geese' include both northern and South American species, but the latter are not really related to the true geese, and have come to look like them because they feed in the same sort of way (Fig. 4).

FIGURE 4. Barnacle Goose *Branta leucopsis* (left) and Upland Sheldgoose *Chloëphaga picta picta* (right).

4 · PRACTICAL DIFFICULTIES IN CLASSIFICATION

As already mentioned, fossil remains are much too scarce to enable one to trace the past evolution of the waterfowl. Hence their affinities have to be inferred from what we know of the living forms. For this purpose, colour and size are of little help, because they are so adaptable to the way of life, and reliance has been placed chiefly on anatomy, both of external parts such as the beak and legs, and of internal organs. Recently, too, court-ship and other displays have been shown to be a valuable guide. But anatomy and behaviour are also adaptable, and it would be helpful to be able to use a feature which does not vary with the way of life. The chemical nature of the white of the egg may prove to be of this type, and this can be analysed by modern biochemical methods (in particular by those which show the sequence of the protein molecules). But while this technique has helped to determine which families of birds are related, research has not yet gone far enough to use it for determining the affinities of species in the same family.

Hence there is not yet enough information of the relationships of the different kinds of waterfowl to each other. For instance, although Delacour completed his book *The Waterfowl of the World* as late as 1964, already two other workers, one studying anatomy and the other behaviour, have reached partly different conclusions from him, and from each other, regarding the affinities of certain species, and if their work is accepted, the classification of the waterfowl will have to be correspondingly modified. One of these 'difficult' species is the Cape Barren Goose *Cereopsis novaehollandiae*, shown in Fig. 5.

FIGURE 5. Cape Barren Goose *Cereopsis novaehollandiae*.

Even, however, if all the biological facts about the living species were known, and even if there were a full fossil record, workers would still differ somewhat from each other on how the waterfowl should be classified, because some of the decisions involved are inevitably arbitrary. The evolution of the water-

14

fowl can be visualised as the branches of a tree coming from a main stem and ending in twigs (the living species). Some branches have produced many twigs, others only one or two, and others have died. Some branches come out close to big branches, others further apart, and some of them, after diverging, have grown close together again. To complete the analogy, the scientific worker is in the position of a man gazing at the top of the tree from above. He cannot see the branches, i.e. the fossil record, and so has to infer the relationships of the twigs to each other from their present positions, and this may be misleading, because some twigs have diverged rapidly, while others, after diverging, have grown closer to each other (like the northern and South American 'geese' mentioned in the previous chapter).

Even, however, if the observer could see all the underlying branches, the classification of the twigs would in part be arbitrary. One might say that all the twigs coming from one small branch should be put in the same genus, and that several small branches coming from a big branch should be treated as separate genera and put in the same subfamily. But things are not so simple, for the branches are not just of two sizes, small and big, but of many different sizes. Hence even if one knew which twigs came from which branch (i.e. which species were closely related), arbitrary judgements would still be needed to decide which of the minor branches merited separate generic names, and which were big enough to be regarded as subfamilies.

There is the further difficulty that a genus can be defined only if the species in it differ in clear-cut ways from all other species. If, for instance, two groups of species differ so greatly from each other that separate genera seem justified, they have, nevertheless, to be put in the same genus if there exist other species which bridge the gap between them, since otherwise there is no place for these intermediate species.

As a result of these various points, the different genera of birds are not strictly comparable. They may contain different numbers of species (from one to sixty), and the degree to which each genus differs in appearance from others also varies greatly. Some workers have been so troubled by these difficulties that they have put all except extremely similar species into separate genera. But when this is done, the number of names becomes excessive, and since many genera contain only one species each, the convenience of grouping related species together breaks down. Nowadays, a reasonable compromise has been reached in most groups of birds, including the waterfowl, and there is fairly good agreement between different workers as to which genera should, or should not, be used, but this is the result of rather arbitrary decisions.

5 · THE NAMING OF SPECIES

The basic unit of classification is the species. Allowing for differences due to age and sex, the members of one species are closely similar to each other in appearance and differ in constant ways from the members of all other species. In the international system of nomenclature invented by Linnaeus, each species of animal and plant bears a scientific name of two words, hence it is called a binomial system. The first word is that of the genus (which usually includes more than one species), and the second is that of the species itself. Both words are normally printed in italics, and a capital is used for the first letter of the generic but not the specific name. (Formerly, a capital letter was used if the specific name is that of a person or place, but this custom has been given up for animals, though it is still used for plants.)

Formally, the specific name is followed by the name of the man who gave it, but this is usually omitted for animals except in works dealing with taxonomy. For instance, the full scientific name of the familiar Mallard or Wild Duck is *Anas platyrhynchos* Linnaeus, which means that, along with other dabbling ducks, it is in the genus *Anas*, and that its specific name *platyrhynchos* was given to it by Linnaeus. In practice, it is often referred to simply as *A. platyrhynchos*. The placing of the author's name in brackets after the specific name, as in the European Shelduck *Tadorna tadorna* (Linnaeus), means that when Linnaeus named it *tadorna*, it was put in a different genus (in this case *Anas*), from which it was removed by later workers. (In animals, the generic name is occasionally the same as the specific name, as in *T. tadorna*, but this practice is not allowed in plant names.)

Particularly when it has already been mentioned on the page concerned, the generic name is often abbreviated to the initial capital letter followed by a full-stop. But a specific name is incomplete without at least the first letter of the generic name in front of it. One reason for this is that species in different genera sometimes have the same specific name. For instance the Baldpate (an American wigeon) is *Anas americana* and the Redhead (an American pochard) is *Aythya americana*, so confusion could arise if their generic name were omitted (and in this case also if only the initial letter of the generic name were used).

Generic names are liable to change when views on relationships change, but the name given to each species should be constant. There have, however, been difficulties about this. For instance, two workers may unwittingly have given different names to the same species. Under these circumstances, the name to be used is settled by priority, i.e. it is the name which was published first, using the 10th edition of 1758 of the *Systema Naturae* of Linnaeus as the starting point. If, however, such a change would mean suppressing a long-established name, with resulting confusion, a special international committee of zoologists has power to declare the long-used name valid (as a *nomen conservandum*').

Confusion may also arise if the original description attached to a particular name makes it uncertain to what species it applies. Nowadays this is always clear because the description of a new species has to be based on a 'type specimen', kept in a museum, to which reference can be made, but this was not

FIGURE 6. Australian *Anas superciliosa* (left) and American *A. rubripes* (right) Black Ducks.

always done in the past. Once again, cases of serious doubt can be resolved by the international committee just mentioned. So far as waterfowl are concerned, earlier difficulties about specific names have been settled. The point is mentioned here simply because, otherwise, the reader might be puzzled to find, in the older bird-books, different specific names from some of those used here.

In addition to its international scientific name, each species has popular or vernacular names, sometimes several in the same language. To help the reader, the usual English name of each

FIGURE 7. Pair of Long-tailed Ducks *Clangula hyemalis*.

species has been given in this booklet with the scientific name. There are no rules about vernacular names and, like all language, they change with time, as anyone can see by referring to the early bird-books. Further, the same vernacular name may be used for different species in different lands. For instance the Black Duck (Fig. 6) means to an American *Anas rubripes*, but to an Australian *Anas superciliosa*. Conversely, the same species may have a different English name in different lands. For instance *Clangula hyemalis* (Fig. 7) is called the Long-tailed Duck in Britain but the Old Squaw in North America. There is, however, a welcome move to make the British and American vernacular bird-names the same, though this is not yet complete.

6 · THE GENERIC NAMES

The use of the same generic name for two species indicates that they are closely related. But how different they have to be from each other to justify separate genera is in part a matter of opinion, and the points discussed in Chapter 4 show that an arbitrary element will always be involved. Linnaeus himself used broad genera, and since many new species have been discovered after his time, many of his original genera have become large, and sometimes unwieldy. Hence many of them have been split up by later workers, which is why the name of Linnaeus is so often found in brackets after a specific name (as explained in the previous chapter).

In some groups of ducks, the splitting of genera probably went too far. For instance Linnaeus put all the European dabbling ducks in the genus *Anas* (the Mallard being *A. platyrhynchos*, the Wigeon *A. penelope*, the Gadwall *A. strepera*, the Teal *A. crecca*, the Pintail *A. acuta* and the Shoveler *A. clypeata*). Later workers put each of these six species into a separate genus (using the names *Anas, Mareca, Chaulelasmus, Nettion* or *Querquedula, Dafila* and *Spatula* respectively). But though, as the illustrations show (Fig. 8), the drakes of these six species look very different (which was why they were later put in separate genera), the ducks look much alike, and these species also resemble each other in anatomy and behaviour, except for the Shoveler, which has a peculiar beak. Moreover, the drakes differ primarily in their colour patterns, which are not usually a good guide to relationships in birds. Hence it is generally agreed that the two workers who, twenty years ago, returned them all to the genus *Anas* were right to do so.

The objection to having six different genera for these species is not merely that it multiplies names, but that it hides their close relationship to each other. But a species must be moved out of a genus if it is not related to the other species in it. For instance the South American Ringed Teal has been known as *Anas leucophrys* since it was named over a century ago, but recent work on its anatomy and behaviour suggest that it really belongs with the perching ducks (tribe Cairinini), and should probably be put in a genus of its own, *Callonetta*. A genus of this latter sort, with only one species, is called a monotypic genus. Such genera are inconvenient, but are needed for species which are not closely related to any others. There are several more of them in the waterfowl, including the Cape Barren Goose *Cereopsis novaehollandiae* and the Long-tailed Duck *Clangula hyemalis*. At the other extreme, the genus *Anas* includes some 36 living species, and is one of the largest found in birds. In all, just over 40 genera are currently used for the waterfowl, with an average of nearly 4 species in each. A full list of the living and recently extinct species has been set out in Appendix 1 (p. 84).

Scientific generic names often correspond with vernacular group names. For instance, all the species of *Anas* are known as dabbling (or surface-feeding) ducks and all those of *Tadorna* as shelducks. Other vernacular names cover more than one genus.

FIGURE 8. Males and females of (from top to bottom) Mallard *Anas platyrhynchos*, Wigeon *A. penelope*, Gadwall *A strepera*, Teal *A. crecca*, Garganey *A. querquedula*, Pintail *A. acuta*, and Shoveler *A. clypeata*.

Thus the word 'goose' includes the species of both *Anser* and *Branta* (and sometimes also the South American 'sheld-geese' *Chloëphaga*), and 'pochard' includes the species of *Netta* and some, but not all, of the species of *Aythya*. Note that a vernacular group name does not start with a capital letter, whereas a specific English name, being a proper noun, does.

7 · THE HIGHER TAXONOMIC GROUPS

The waterfowl, like many other families of birds, are divided into subfamilies. For reasons already discussed, such subdivisions are meant to show relationships, so need not be of similar size. In fact the Australian Magpie Goose *Anseranas semipalmata* is considered so peculiar that it is placed in a subfamily by itself, the Anseranatinae. The other two subfamilies are the Anserinae with 28 species, and the Anatinae with nearly 120 species. (Note that subfamilies end in 'inae' and that one of them usually bears the same name as the whole family.)

In the waterfowl, but not in most other birds, modern workers have used a further category intermediate between the subfamily and the genus, namely the tribe. The reader need not remember the names of the different tribes or subfamilies of waterfowl, but they give an overall survey of the group, so have been set out below.

1 Subfamily Anseranatinae : 1 species, the Magpie Goose.

2 Subfamily Anserinae : 2 tribes.
   (i) Dendrocygnini : 8 species of whistling or tree ducks, a tropical group.
   (ii) Anserini : 6 species of swans and 14 of true (northern) geese.

FIGURE 9. One example of each of the nine tribes of waterfowl.

Anserini
(Mute Swan & Red-
breasted Goose)

Cygnus olor

Anseranatini
(Magpie Goose
Anseranas semipalmata)

Branta ruficollis

Tadornini
(Shelduck *Tadorna tadorna*)

Dendrocygnini
(White-faced
Whistling Duck *Dendrocygna
viduata*)

Anatini
(Shoveler
Anas clypeata)

Aythyini
(Tufted Duck
Aythya fuligula)

Cairinini
(Mandarin *Aix galericulata*)

Mergini
(Red-breasted
Merganser
Mergus serrator)

Oxyurini
(North American
Ruddy Duck
Oxyura jamaicensis)

3 Subfamily Anatinae : 6 tribes.
   (i) Tadornini : 20 species of sheld-geese and shelducks.
   (ii) Anatini : 43 species of dabbling (or surface-feeding) ducks.
   (iii) Aythyini : 15 species of pochards (freshwater diving ducks).
   (iv) Cairinini : 12 diverse species of perching ducks, mainly tropical.
   (v) Mergini : 20 species of sea ducks, nearly all northern.
   (vi) Oxyurini : 9 species of stifftails.

The distinctive features of the birds in each of these tribes can be seen in the illustrations. Many of those in the same tribe are obviously related to each other, but others, notably in the Cairinini, are more diverse, and yet others cannot certainly be placed. Further research will probably show that some of the last group are much modified members of one of the existing tribes, others may be genuinely intermediate between two tribes, and yet others should perhaps be put in separate tribes on their own. Since an arbitrary element enters into such decisions, no two workers have been in complete agreement. The eider ducks, for instance, are sometimes put in the Mergini and sometimes in a tribe of their own. It has also been suggested that the swans should be moved from the Anserini to a tribe of their own, and the Ringed Teal *Anas* (or *Callonetta*) *leucophrys* has recently been moved from the Anatini to the Cairinini. However these and other recent suggestions affect relatively few of the species, and they are unimportant so far as this book is concerned, except to show that certainty in classification is unattainable. There are also a few doubts at the level of the subfamily. In particular, the Cape Barren Goose *Cereopsis novaehollandiae* (shown in Fig. 5, p. 14) should perhaps be moved from the Anatinae (tribe Tadornini) to the Anserinae. It may be wondered whether it is worth while to have a separate subfamily just for the Magpie Goose.

The categories above the family need only brief mention. The

Anatidae together with three species of screamers Anhimidae (which are also kept at the Wildfowl Trust), comprise the order Anseriformes (all bird orders end in 'formes'). The order Anseriformes is one of nearly thirty orders of living birds which together comprise the class Aves, and the birds, with other classes such as the fish, reptiles and mammals, comprise the phylum Vertebrata, the backboned animals, which with other phyla comprise the Animal Kingdom.

8 · THE NAMING OF SUBSPECIES

Many species of birds, including various waterfowl, differ somewhat in colour or size in different parts of their breeding range. The first such forms to be described were so different from each other that they were treated as separate species. In old bird-books, for instance, the Teal *Anas crecca* of Europe was regarded as a different species from the American Green-winged Teal *Anas carolinensis*. The females of these two birds look very alike, but while the males have generally similar coloration, the European bird has more creamy lines on the face, the American bird has a broad crescent-shaped white band on the side of the breast, and they also differ somewhat in the colour of the shoulders and breast, so that they are easily distinguished in the field (see Fig. 10).

It came gradually to be realised that such geographical variations are common in birds, though the differences are usually less striking than those between the two forms of teal just mentioned. Hence it became impossible to treat all of them as separate species, and after long and often heated discussion, it was decided to add a third 'subspecific' name after that of the species, to indicate a geographical race. The subspecies breeding in the area from which the species was first described bears the name of the species (and it is called the 'typical' race, because the type specimen belongs to it, but it need not be 'typical' in any other sense). Thus the European Teal is now called *Anas crecca crecca* (often abbreviated to *A.c. crecca*), while the North American form is called *Anas crecca carolinensis*.

FIGURE 10. European *Anas crecca crecca* (left) and American (right) *A.c. carolinensis* Teal drakes.

Further research has shown that every population of a species may differ somewhat in its hereditary make-up from all the rest, and in birds this is often shown by slight differences in average measurements or shade of plumage. For a time, museum workers tried to give a separate name to every local variant, but this became unmanageable and absurd. In particular, many species show a gradual change, or 'cline', in size or colour over a big area, and in such cases it may be impossible to draw any definite line between one population and another. Nowadays, separate subspecific names are used only for well-marked forms, and a convenient practice is the '75 per cent rule', on which basis a local population is given a separate subspecific name only if at least three-quarters of the specimens can be reliably separated from those of other populations.

At the opposite end of the scale, some geographical forms are so distinct that it is hard to know whether they should be treated as subspecies or species. In the case of the Teal just mentioned, there is now general agreement that the European and North American forms should be regarded as belonging to

26

the same species. But there is serious doubt over certain other waterfowl. To cite only one instance, the Bean Goose *Anser fabalis* breeds across the far north of Europe and Asia, where it is divided into five subspecies which intergrade with each other. In Greenland, Iceland and Spitsbergen, it is replaced by the Pink-footed Goose *Anser brachyrhynchus*, which can be distinguished in the field from the European race of the Bean Goose by its much shorter beak, which is pink-and-black instead of yellow-and-black, and by its pink instead of yellowish orange legs. Nevertheless, it looks much more like a Bean Goose than any other species, and though it does not intergrade with it, some modern workers think that it should be treated merely as a subspecies, though others retain it as a full species. This is a genuine intermediate case, and there is no certain answer. Some further examples will be mentioned in Chapter 11.

At one time, each subspecies of a species was also given a separate English name, but this clumsy practice has been largely abandoned. It is, however, useful to have separate English names for the small proportion of subspecies which can be distinguished in the field. Hence the Pink-footed Goose will doubtless keep its English name even if it were agreed to be a subspecies of the Bean Goose.

9 · THE NATURE OF SUBSPECIES

This concludes all that need be said here about the principles of classification, and it is now time to consider the biogeographical significance of the differences between different forms. For this purpose, it is simplest to start with the smallest differences, those between geographically isolated populations. As mentioned in the previous section, these range from differences in average measurements or colour so slight that they are not worth naming, up to differences as great as those which distinguish some full species.

First, two more examples of well-marked subspecies may be mentioned. Each winter, several thousand wild White-fronted Geese *Anser albifrons* (Fig. 11) spend the winter in the fields round the Wildfowl Trust alongside the River Severn in Gloucestershire. These belong to the race *A.a. albifrons*, which breeds in arctic Europe, whereas in Ireland there occurs the Greenland race of the same species *A.a. flavirostris*, which has darker plumage and an orange instead of a pink beak. It is

FIGURE 11. European *Anser albifrons albifrons* (a), Greenland *A.a. flavirostris* (b) and Lesser *A. erythropus* (c) White-fronted Goose.

therefore as easy to tell in the field from the European race *A.a. albifrons* as is a different species, the Lesser White-fronted Goose *Anser erythropus*, which is similar in colour to *A.a. albifrons* but smaller. However, *A. erythropus* is classified as a full species, not a subspecies, because it breeds in arctic Europe, near to, but without interbreeding with, *A. albifrons*. As a second example, the drake of the European and North American form of the Mallard *Anas p. platyrhynchos* is strikingly different from the female (Fig. 12), with a green head, white ring round the neck, reddish brown breast and pale grey on the wings; but in the Florida subspecies *A.p. fulvigula* and the Mexican subspecies *A.p. diazi*, the male is dull brown, like the female. Such a big difference between subspecies is rare.

FIGURE 12. Pair of Mallards *Anas p. platyrhynchos.*

Each subspecies breeds true, which means that the differences between subspecies are hereditary. For example, the heaviest subspecies of the Canada Goose *Branta canadensis* is four times as heavy as the smallest, but young born in captivity grow to the size which is characteristic of their own subspecies, almost irrespective of the amount of food given to them. Again, some subspecies of the Canada Goose are pale and others dark, but though, as shown later, this is correlated with the climate where they live, captive goslings of each race assume as adults the colour of their parents, irrespective of the climate where they are reared. As a familiar illustration of the same principle, the children of Englishmen, Chinamen and Africans retain

29

their characteristic colouring whether they are born and raised in England, China or Africa.

The species of waterfowl are divided into subspecies to a much smaller extent than many other kinds of birds. Just over two-thirds of them are not subdivided at all, these being called mono-typic species, while many others have only two subspecies each. As many as five or six races are found only in the Bean Goose *Anser fabalis*, Mallard *Anas platyrhynchos*, Cinnamon Teal *Anas cyanoptera*, Torrent Duck *Merganetta armata* and Common Eider *Somateria mollissima*, while the Canada Goose *Branta canadensis* is quite exceptional, with 12 subspecies.

Subspecies are much more frequent in geese than ducks. For instance, in the species breeding in northern Europe, Asia and America, the average number of subspecies per species is three for the geese but only one and a quarter for the dabbling ducks (based on 12 and 13 species respectively). This difference can be explained through the degree of isolation of the populations concerned. The geese of a given species which breed in one area form into flocks and migrate together to a common wintering area, while individuals of the same species from another breeding area spend the winter elsewhere; hence the birds from each breeding area are segregated from those of other areas. But in the northern dabbling ducks, individuals from widely separated breeding areas spend the winter together, and as they form pairs in winter, they freely interbreed, so that local populations are not isolated.

The influence of isolation, or the lack of it, is also shown by two further examples. The dabbling ducks breeding in tropical Asia, Africa and America are normally resident, not migratory, so that local populations tend to be more isolated from each other than are those of the northern migratory species; correspondingly, the average number of subspecies is higher in the tropical than the northern birds, being just over two per species. In contrast, the dabbling ducks of the interior of Australia are nomadic, moving to breed in widely separated areas in different years according to where rain, which comes irregularly, has fallen. Hence local populations are not isolated and, correspondingly, no dabbling ducks are divided into subspecies within Australia.

It is not known how long a new subspecies of waterfowl might take to evolve. However, the House Sparrow *Passer domesticus* was introduced from Europe to the eastern United States about a century ago and has spread rapidly across the continent, where it has already become divided into geographical races which differ to a moderate extent from each other, chiefly in the shade of the upper parts and in size. The date at which the House Sparrow reached various parts of the United States is known, so it can be said with confidence that some of these subspecies are only thirty to fifty years old. Similarly the European Goldfinch *Carduelis carduelis* was introduced to Bermuda, and had become a well-marked geographical race in less than 60 years. Until these observations were made, biologists had supposed that a much longer period was needed for the evolution of a new subspecies.

10 · THE SUBSPECIES OF CANADA GOOSE

The situation in the Canada Goose *Branta canadensis* is so unusual for a waterfowl that it deserves separate treatment. The map (Fig. 13) shows the breeding ranges of the 12 subspecies. Their ranges in winter have not been shown, but in general those races which breed furthest north spend the winter furthest south. Each of the six coastal subspecies occupies a relatively small breeding area and is sharply separated in appearance from other races, but the six inland subspecies intergrade with each other near the boundaries of their ranges, which have therefore been shown by dotted instead of continuous lines on the map. Moreover the inland populations could be further subdivided on the basis of average measurements, but these minor subdivisions are not sufficiently distinct to warrant separate names. They show, however, that geographical variation is not restricted to the named subspecies.

Size tends to be larger in the inland than the coastal subspecies and in the southern than the northern ones. To cite the extremes, the average weight of the adult male is only 1·6 kg in the race *B.c. minima* but four times as great in the race *B.c. maxima*, in which the largest individuals are seven times as heavy as the smallest of *B.c. minima*. This is the greatest known difference in size found between two subspecies in any species of bird.

FIGURE 13. Map of breeding ranges of 12 subspecies of Canada Geese.

In birds and mammals, subspecies of the same species tend to be larger in colder than warmer climates (Bergmann's rule), and this tendency is so widespread that it is presumably adaptive. The usual explanation is that the heat lost by a bird is proportional to its surface area, but the heat produced is proportional to its volume, so that a larger bird loses proportionately less heat than a smaller one; hence a bird could compensate for the extra heat lost in a colder climate by evolving larger size. At first sight the Canada Goose is an exception to this trend, as the smallest subspecies breed furthest north; but they spend the winter furthest south, so selection for body-size has evidently operated in winter, not summer. A similar situation is found in the Ringed Plover *Charadrius hiaticula* in Europe, where a small arctic subspecies breeds further north, but winters further south, than larger subspecies.

While the subspecies of Canada Goose vary in size mainly from north to south, they vary in colour mainly from east to west, the six western races being darker than the six eastern. This is in line with another general trend found in birds and other animals, namely for subspecies of the same species to be darker in wetter than drier climates (Gloger's rule). It is curious that, though this trend is widespread, its adaptive value is still uncertain.

For the sake of completeness, brief mention should be made here of the Ne-Ne or Hawaiian Goose *Branta sandvicensis*, as it is generally considered to have evolved from the Canada Goose, but is so distinctive that it is treated as a separate species. It is smaller than all except the smallest races of the Canada Goose and is as pale as the palest races. Further, most of the head and neck are buff instead of black, with peculiar ridges on the neck, and the goslings are grey instead of yellowish brown. Although it can swim, it lives to a much greater extent on land than does the Canada Goose, and as an adaptation for this, it has proportionately longer legs and toes, and reduced webs between the toes. It also has a proportionately longer beak. These are much bigger differences than those between any two races of the Canada Goose, but they have evidently arisen in isolation in the same kind of way.

Another exceptional group of subspecies are the ducks breeding on remote islands. The land birds of such islands are famous for their endemic forms, *i.e.* peculiar native forms, but the ducks show comparatively little variation, though more than they do elsewhere. Even on the Galapagos Islands, where the extraordinary finches and mocking-birds discovered by Darwin in 1835 gave him his first idea of evolution, the resident duck is merely a subspecies of a South American species, the Bahama Pintail *Anas bahamensis*. The evolution of landbirds has been even more remarkable in the Hawaiian archipelago than in the Galapagos, but the Hawaiian duck is again a subspecies of a mainland species, this time of the Mallard *Anas platyrhynchos*, with another form on adjacent Laysan. Similarly the Fanning Islands (on the Equator in the Pacific) had a subspecies of another northern species, the Gadwall *Anas strepera*, though it is now extinct.

Two other archipelagos with an endemic subspecies of duck are in the subantarctic. Kerguelen and the adjoining Crozet Islands have a form of the Northern Pintail *Anas acuta*, and South Georgia has a form of the Chilean Pintail *Anas georgica*. Finally, the Auckland Islands off New Zealand have an endemic form of the Chestnut Teal *Anas castanea* (which also breeds in New Zealand and Australia); they also have the Grey Duck *Anas superciliosa*, which is not a peculiar form but of the same subspecies as in New Zealand. All these island forms except the last are so distinctive that they were formerly treated as full species, but each of them shows clear resemblances to a particular mainland species, and nowadays they are usually treated as subspecies.

That, except on the Aucklands, only one species of duck breeds on each of the islands concerned suggests that, ecologically speaking, there is room for only one. That it is a different species in each archipelago is presumably due to the historical factor of which species happened to arrive there first, this being influenced by which species breed on the nearest mainland. All the island forms are of similar size to each other and smaller than their mainland ancestors, the reduction in size being greatest in those derived from large species, like the Mallard, Gadwall and Northern Pintail. Presumably, medium size is that best adapted to the living conditions for ducks on remote islands.

FIGURE 14. Laysan *Anas platyrhynchos Laysanensis* (a), Hawaiian *A.p. wyvilliana* (b) and Northern *A.p. platyrhynchos* (c) Mallard.

In colour, the females of these various ducks differ only slightly from their mainland ancestors, but some of them have a duller wing-patch or head-markings. Five of these island forms are descended from mainland species in which the male has strikingly distinct plumage, but in all of them the male has largely lost this colouring, and looks more or less like the female. This holds in the Hawaiian and Laysan Mallard (Fig. 14), the

Fanning Island Gadwall, the Kerguelen Pintail and the Auckland Island Chestnut Teal. (The male is also coloured like the female in the other island forms, but as this also applies to their mainland ancestors, it has no special significance.) As discussed in Chapter 16, distinctive male plumage probably helps the female to mate with a male of her own species, and the wing-mirror and head-markings of the female may likewise help in specific recognition. There is presumably much less need for such recognition marks on remote islands with only one resident duck than on the mainland where several species usually occur together.

Bird-books may give the impression that subspecies of the same species differ from each other only in size or colour, but this is partly because, in most species, size and colour are the only differences that have been studied. The island ducks also differ from their mainland ancestors in feeding habits, bodily proportions and the number and size of their eggs. Though all of them are derived from freshwater species which eat primarily vegetable matter, several of them feed partly in salt water and several of them take much animal food, hence they take a broader range of foods than their mainland ancestors. The Kerguelen Pintail has a relatively shorter beak than the Northern Pintail, probably correlated with its feeding partly on crustacea, while the Auckland Island Duck has a proportionately larger beak than the New Zealand form, for unknown reasons. The most specialised of them in diet is the Laysan Duck, which feeds on insects on land, and, correlated with its walking on land, it has a proportionately longer tarsus than the Mallard. A bigger anatomical difference is found in the Chestnut Teal, of which the Australian form flies strongly, the New Zealand form poorly, and the Auckland Island form is flightless, with much reduced wings (Fig. 15). A few other birds on remote islands have lost the power of flight, the most famous being the extinct Dodo *Raphus cucullatus* of Mauritius. Finally, the island ducks have relatively larger eggs and smaller clutches than the mainland forms. As discussed in Chapter 21, a larger egg gives rise to a larger duckling at hatching, which may be advantageous where food for the young is sparse, even though, due to limited food reserves in the female, this may necessitate a smaller clutch.

FIGURE 15. Chestnut *Anas castanea* (a), New Zealand Brown *A. aucklandica chlorotis* (b) and Auckland Island *A.a. aucklandica* (c) Teal.

The islands where these ducks live are sufficiently isolated to have allowed the birds to evolve hereditary differences from their mainland ancestors. But isolation does not, in itself, explain the kind of differences that they have evolved. The fact that all of them are smaller than their mainland relatives could hardly be a coincidence, and presumably means that smaller size is advantageous for them. That nearly all of them have more generalised diets than their mainland relatives may also be advantageous, if there is a reduction in the foods suitable for ducks on islands. These points suggest that on remote islands, with their reduced ecological diversity, one medium-sized species of duck is more efficient than two or more specialised species, and eliminates such other species through competition if they arrive. In fact, several other species of ducks have been seen on some of the islands concerned, but they do not remain to breed, presumably because any that try to do so are eliminated in competition with the resident species.

The Laysan Duck differs from the rest in having a specialised diet, which might be linked with the absence of other land birds eating the foods which it takes, and as already mentioned, its unusually long legs are presumably an adaptation for walking on land. Long legs and toes have also been evolved by the Ne-Ne or Hawaiian Goose *Branta sandvicensis*, which is likewise more terrestrial than its presumed ancestor, the Canada Goose *Branta canadensis*. Indeed, the Ne-Ne might have been included in this chapter as another island waterfowl. But, as already explained, it has evolved such big differences that it is treated as a full species, and is sometimes put in a genus on its own.

12 · THE TRANSITION FROM SUBSPECIES TO SPECIES

As mentioned in Chapter 8, the Pink-footed Goose replaces the Bean Goose geographically but does not intergrade with it, so some workers treat it as a full species *Anser brachyrhynchus*, but others regard it as a subspecies of the Bean Goose *A. fabalis* (Fig. 16). Similar dispute has arisen over the island ducks discussed in the previous chapter. The Australian Chestnut Teal, the New Zealand Brown Teal and the flightless Auckland Island Duck replace each other geographically and are sufficiently alike to show that they are more closely related to each other than to any other ducks (Fig. 15). Formerly, they were treated as separate species, *A. castanea*, *A. chlorotis* and *A. aucklandica* respectively, but everyone nowadays puts the two latter in one species, and some workers think that this should also apply to *A. castanea*, even though it does not breed within a thousand miles of the New Zealand form.

Again, the Laysan Duck is so different from the Mallard that it would have been extremely hard to decide its ancestry if the Hawaiian Duck had not been intermediate in appearance, presumably because the Hawaiian Duck was its immediate ancestor. Various modern workers treat the Laysan and Hawaiian Ducks as subspecies of the Mallard, but again, they do not intergrade and do not meet in nature, so other workers retain them as full species, *A. laysanensis* and *A. wyvilliana* respectively. Yet again, though the Kerguelen Pintail looks like a subspecies of the Northern Pintail, the breeding areas of the two forms are separated by about 80 degrees of latitude, and no subspecies of the Pintail breeds in between.

FIGURE 16. Pink-footed *Anser (fabalis) brachyrhynchus* (left) and Western Bean *A.f. fabalis* (right) Goose.

Such instances have given rise to fruitless arguments as to the correct name to use. But as has often happened in science, something that was first regarded merely as a nuisance has become the basis of a new theory. For many years, there was great dispute as to how new species might originate, but enough is now known to say that, at least in birds, the only populations with hereditary differences less than those which separate different species are geographical races or subspecies of the same species, and they show every gradation from forms just separable from each other on average measurements to forms as different as full species. The conclusion is clear that, at least in birds, new species arise from geographically isolated populations.

The origin of new species by this means is seen mostly clearly in a few kinds of birds, such as the Herring and Lesser Black-backed Gull complex, or the Great Tit *Parus major-P. minor* complex, in which a long series of geographical subspecies extends over two or more continents but, in one area, two forms derived from widely separated parts of this series have met and do not interbreed. Hence there they have become full species, though elsewhere they are linked by geographical races. But no instance of this sort is known in waterfowl.

It was formerly thought that a new species of bird might arise from populations living in the same area but in different habitats, but this view has been discarded because no transitional stages are known, *i.e.* there are no subspecies of one species which differ in habitat but not in geographical range. Further, it is now appreciated that different subspecies have many hereditary differences, and for these to become established, much greater isolation is needed than any that could arise between different individuals of one species living in the same area though in different habitats. Probably the same holds true in at least most of the higher animals, but in plants new species can arise in other ways than by geographical isolation.

Bird populations which live in different geographical areas are called 'allopatric' and those which live in the same area (but not necessarily in the same habitat) are called 'sympatric'. Hence the theory that new species arise from geographical races is called 'allopatric speciation', and the idea that they may arise from populations living in different habitats in the same area is called 'sympatric speciation'. All subspecies of the same species are, of course, allopatric. Many related species are sympatric, and if they are, *i.e.* if they live in the same area but do not interbreed, it is certain that they are different species. The difficulty in deciding whether such forms as the Laysan Duck and Kerguelen Pintail are subspecies or full species is that they are allopatric with the Mallard and Northern Pintail respectively, hence one cannot tell whether, if they met in the wild, they would interbreed with them or keep separate.

13 · COLOUR PHASES

The Snow Goose *Anser caerulescens*, which has white plumage except for its black wing-tips, breeds in arctic Siberia, arctic North America and north-west Greenland, and is divided into a larger eastern and smaller western subspecies. But mixed with eastern populations of the smaller race occur birds of the same size, proportions, voice and habits, which differ markedly in appearance, as they have bluish grey upper-parts and brownish grey underparts, with a white head and upper neck (Fig. 17). These Blue Geese breed in mixed colonies with Lesser Snow Geese and often interbreed, though they have some preference for mating with individuals of their own colour. As they breed in the same area they are not separate subspecies, and as they freely interbreed they are not separate species, so they are regarded as colour phases, but how they arose and why they persist is not known. Colour phases are found in a few other birds. For instance the Arctic Skua *Stercorarius parasiticus* may be either dark brown all over, or brown above and mainly white below.

Subsequent discussion will be helped by a knowledge of simple genetics, which may be illustrated from the domestic Mallard. Some breeds of the latter are termed 'dusky', because the ducklings are black above and dark grey below, instead of yellow patterned with brown, as in the wild type (Fig. 18),

FIGURE 17. Blue (left) and Lesser (right) Snow Goose *Anser caerulescens*.

while the adults, though they differ less, are also darker and less clearly marked than those of the wild type. The dusky character depends on a single hereditary unit, or gene. When a pure-bred dusky bird is crossed with a pure-bred wild type, the offspring receive a dusky gene from one parent and a wild-type gene from the other; nevertheless, all look like the wild type, so this wild-type gene is said to be dominant, and the dusky gene is said to be recessive. When these cross-bred birds are mated together, their offspring (the grandchildren of the original cross) have an equal chance of receiving a dusky or a wild-type gene from each of their parents. Hence a quarter of them receive a dusky gene from each parent and look dusky, a quarter receive a wild-type gene from each parent and are pure-bred wild type, and the rest receive one gene of each type, but look like the wild type. Hence among the grandchildren there is one dusky bird to every three which look like the wild type.

When Darwin wrote the *Origin of Species* in 1859, he did not understand how hereditary changes or mutations could become established in a population, instead of being swamped by cross-breeding with the normal type. However experiments like those just mentioned show that mutations are not swamped after crossing with the wild type, but may reappear in later generations. Curiously, the early geneticists did not think that the mutations which they studied were concerned in natural evolution. This was partly because they were considered too large to be the units of gradual evolutionary change. But it was natural, at the start, to study mutations producing conspicuous effects, and it is now known that mutations with extremely small effects are inherited in the same kind of way.

FIGURE 18. Normal and 'dusky' ducklings of Mallard.

A more serious difficulty was that mutations away from the wild type are normally both harmful and recessive, which suggests that they could not provide the basis for the evolution of new adaptations. But it is now known that each part of the body is affected by many genes, not just one, though some of them have only a slight influence. Hence if a mutation arises with harmful effects, natural selection favours those individuals with a combination of other genes which modify the harmful effects, first making them recessive and later, perhaps, eliminating them. Conversely, any beneficial effects of a mutation tend to be increased by the selection of modifying genes and to become dominant. The wild type of every animal has been subject to natural selection for many generations, so that it is well adapted to its natural environment. Hence any different mutation, like 'dusky' in the Mallard, is likely to be harmful in the wild, so the animal is likely to have evolved genes to make it recessive. On

43

this view, it was to be expected that mutation away from the wild type would be both harmful and recessive, as they usually are, and it is now generally agreed that natural selection is responsible for this and for the evolution of dominance.

From individuals kept in captivity, it is known that when two Snow Geese breed together their offspring are white, but when two Blue Geese, or a Blue and a Snow Goose, breed together, their offspring are usually blue but occasionally white. The proportion of blue to white individuals in these latter crosses is not reliably known, but this evidence suggests that blue is dominant and white recessive. The situation is not entirely simple, however, as rare intermediate individuals exist, with a white head, neck and underparts but dark upper parts. This indicates that one or more modifying genes may also be involved. Further, the fact that neither the Blue nor the Snow Goose has eliminated the other in the wild shows that the selective balance between them is complex. Moreover this balance varies both locally and with time, since Blue Geese are commonest in the eastern and southern parts of the range of the Lesser Snow, and they are at the present time extending their range further west. As yet, the position is not fully understood.

14 · DOMESTIC BREEDS OF WATERFOWL

Four species of waterfowl have been domesticated by man, and by choosing to breed only from those individuals with particular features, man has been able to change their appearance drastically. Darwin, who used pigeons as his example, pointed out that the selection of hereditary variations in domestic animals by

FIGURE 19. Domestic breeds of Waterfowl. The Mallard *Anas platyrhynchos* (a) has produced the Aylesbury (b), Crested (c) and Khaki Campbell (d). The Greylag *Anser anser* (e) has produced the farmyard goose (f). The Swan Goose *A. cygnoides* (g) has produced the Chinese Goose (h). The Wild Muscovy Duck *Cairina moschata* (i) has produced the domestic form (j).

man provides a parallel with the action of natural selection in the wild. The chief difference is that artificial selection can produce changes much more quickly, because man can usually keep his favoured types alive.

There are no records of domestic forms of the Mallard *Anas platyrhynchos* until about a thousand years ago, but since then, as shown in the illustration (Fig. 19), some striking breeds have been produced. For instance, the wild drake Mallard weighs about 1·2 kg, but the drake Aylesbury and Rouen ducks weigh just over 4 kg (about 9 lb). Again, the colour differs in different breeds, and some of them are white all over. Further, the wild Mallard in the course of a year lays a clutch of 10 eggs, and perhaps a second rather smaller clutch if the first is destroyed, say 17 eggs in a year; but the domestic breeds such as the Indian Runner and Khaki Campbell lay an egg nearly every day throughout the year. A few other breeds, such as the Crested Duck, have been bred for ornament. The resulting differences in appearance look much greater than those between the Mallard and other wild species of dabbling ducks. Nevertheless the various breeds mate freely and successfully with each other and with the wild type of Mallard and the differences between them are in essence simpler than those between different wild species, and depend on many fewer hereditary differences.

The Greylag Goose *Anser anser* has been domesticated for longer than the Mallard, as there are paintings of it on Egyptian frescoes of about 2000 B.C. As in the Mallard, the largest breeds are about three times as heavy as the wild bird, indeed some are so heavy that they cannot fly. Again, some races are white all over, instead of grey like the wild form. Another species, the Swan Goose *Anser cygnoides*, was domesticated by the Chinese, and has given rise to the 'Chinese Goose', which withstands a tropical climate better than do domestic forms of the Greylag. Finally there is the Muscovy Duck *Cairina moschata*, which did not, of course, come from Muscovy (Russia), any more than the Wild Turkey *Meleagris gallopavo* came from Turkey. Both were domesticated by the tropical American Indians and were brought back to Europe by the Spanish conquistadores. Muscovy Ducks have been bred partly for size, and in addition the drakes have red wattles, which are not found in the wild birds.

Bones of the Mallard and Greylag Goose indistinguishable from those of wild individuals alive today have been found fossilised in Pliocene deposits, which means that these species have remained unchanged in size and proportions for between one and ten million years. Yet, through man, they have been drastically changed in a few thousand years. This is not because mutations occur more often under domestication than in the wild, but because any mutations which arise can be preserved and stabilised much more quickly by man than by natural selection. This comparison is not altogether fair, however, because the natural environment of the Mallard and Greylag Goose may well be the same now as it was ten million years ago, and since the birds are well adapted to it, natural selection will tend to eliminate, rather than preserve, any new mutations that arise in the wild state. Because natural selection is the main agent of evolutionary change, we tend to forget that its usual influence is to keep an animal constant, through modifying or eliminating new mutations, which are normally unfavourable. Natural selection may produce rapid changes when the environment changes, but this does not often happen. It may be added that the bones of eight other living species of waterfowl have been found fossil in Pliocene deposits.*

15 · HYBRID DUCKS

The main differences between different species of waterfowl, like those between different subspecies of the same species, are hereditary. When the male of one species breeds with the

* The Whistling Swan *Cygnus columbianus*, Gadwall *Anas strep*era, Teal *A. crecca*, Garganey *A. querquedula*, Shoveler *A. clypeata*, Pochard *Aythya ferina*, Ring-necked Duck *A. collaris* and Bufflehead *Bucephala albeola*.

female of another, the offspring are intermediate between the two species in appearance, but if the hybrids mate with each other, their young are of a great variety of types. This shows that the two parent species differ in very many, not just a few, hereditary factors; hence many different combinations of characters can occur in the grandchildren. Earlier workers had sometimes supposed that, if two species look rather alike, they differ in only a few genes, but this is wrong. Also, because each species differs from others in many genes, a new species cannot be produced quickly by natural selection. The quickest known example in animals has occurred in moths of the genus *Hedyleptis* in the Hawaiian Islands, which are confined as larvae to banana plants introduced to the islands only a thousand years ago.

Hybrids between two species of birds often die in the egg, others as young, while many of those that reach full size are sterile. As discussed in Chapter 13, each species has evolved many genes which modify the harmful effects of others. But in a hybrid individual, one set of genes comes from one species and the other set from another species, so that the hybrid often possesses genes with harmful effects that are not adequately modified by other genes. This may result in bodily defects, and the reproductive cells are specially sensitive, so that sterility is common. Further, even if the hybrid becomes fully grown, it has to compete in the wild with pure-bred individuals of both parent species, and it is likely to be less well adapted to the environment than either of them.*

Different species of waterfowl rarely interbreed in the wild,

* The genes are carried on microscopic structures, the chromosomes, which are normally in pairs, each individual receiving one set from each of its parents. But to this there is one exception, the chromosome which helps to determine sex, of which the male bird has two and the female only one (in most animals it is the other way about). This means that a female bird hybrid has one group of its genes entirely from one of the two parent species, and any adverse effects of these genes are particularly unlikely to be modified by others. This is probably why, in birds, the hybrids that survive are much more often male than female.

but they often do in captivity. Further, the resulting hybrids survive better in captivity than in the wild, perhaps because enemies are much scarcer and there is no competition for food. Probably most of the hybrid ducks seen in the wild in recent years have escaped from captivity. In captivity some of the hybrids may breed in their turn. Captive Mallard have produced young with 40 other species of waterfowl, some of them in different genera or tribes. Moreover some of those hybrids have bred successfully with hybrids of a different species-cross, to produce 'multiple hybrids'.

One pond at the Wildfowl Trust is set apart for hybrid ducks.

FIGURE 20. Hybrid waterfowl. In upper half, drake Tufted Duck *Aythya fuligula* (a) and drake Pochard *A. ferina* (b) with drake hybrid (c) between these two species. In lower half, drake Shelduck *Tadorna tadorna* (d) and drake Eider *Somateria mollissima* (e) with drake hybrid (f) between these two species.

49

By comparing them with the genuine species on other ponds, it is often possible to recognize, or at least to guess, the parent species, but this is not always easy. Some years ago, for instance, ornithologists became excited by a strange duck on a stretch of water near Oxford. This was first identified as a Lesser Scaup *Aythya affinis*, an American species which is extremely rare in Britain. Later it was proved to be a hybrid (Fig. 20) between a Tufted Duck *Aythya fuligula* and a Pochard *A. ferina*.*

16 · SPECIFIC RECOGNITION CHARACTERS

Since new species originate from geographically isolated sub-species, what happens when, through a change in range, two subspecies meet in the same breeding area? If they are not very different, they will probably interbreed and eventually merge. But if they have become very different then, as explained in the previous chapter, their genes will not combine well in any hybrid offspring, so the latter are likely to survive less well than pure-bred offspring of either species. In that situation, an individual will leave more offspring if it mates with a member of its own and not the other species, so it will be advantageous if it can distinguish its own kind and recognition marks will tend to be evolved.

The northern dabbling ducks in the genus *Anas* migrate for the winter to warmer areas, where members of several species often occur together on the same stretch of water. Here the pairs are formed, so that a female in search of a mate meets indi-

---

* At one time, it was thought that new species might arise from hybrids between other species. The duck of the Mariana Islands in the Pacific, formerly called Oustalet's Duck *Anas oustaleti*, is now considered to be a hybrid between Mallard *A. platyrhynchos* from the north and Grey Duck *A. superciliosa* from the south; it is not constant in type but highly variable, so is not really a new species.

viduals of several other species. That is presumably why the male of each species has evolved distinctive plumage (Fig. 21), though it has not actually been proved that the female uses this as a guide. The females of these species are much more like each other than are the males, probably because all of them need brown plumage with darker markings to conceal them on the nest from enemies. But even they possess what is probably a recognition mark, an iridescent patch of colour, the mirror or speculum, on the wing, which is a characteristic colour in each species.

While the male's distinctive plumage and the female's wing-patch probably help in specific recognition, they are a potential danger in making them conspicuous to enemies. It is therefore significant that the female's wing-patch is normally revealed only in flight, and in particular it is hidden when she is sitting on the eggs. Further, the male has no special need for concealing colouring during the breeding season, as he takes no part in incubation or raising the young. But shortly afterwards he becomes temporarily flightless during the moult, so is probably more vulnerable than usual to enemies, and for this period he changes temporarily into full cryptic plumage, the 'eclipse' dress, which is very like that of the female.

The northern migratory species of pochards and sea ducks also form pairs in mixed flocks in the winter or early spring, and in them also, the drake of each species has distinctive bright plumage, while the female is much duller but usually has a distinctive white wing-bar. In contrast, as mentioned in Chapter 11, the males of the ducks breeding on remote islands do not have distinctive plumage, even though they may be derived from mainland forms which possess it, probably because there is only one resident species on each island, so that the female can hardly select a mate of the wrong species. In tropical and subtropical ducks, likewise, the male tends to be coloured like the female. This holds even for the Mexican and Florida subspecies of the Mallard, as mentioned in Chapter 9. The reason is not known. There is no evidence to suggest that tropical ducks are more subject to predation and so have greater need of concealing colouring than those at high northern latitudes, and though they come in contact with fewer other species than the northern forms, one might think that they would have some, if a reduced, need for recognition marks.

In geese, unlike nearly all ducks, the male helps to guard the nest and later helps in escorting the young. Probably, therefore, the male has need for concealing colouring, and this may be why male geese are dully coloured like the females. Further there may be less need for specific recognition, as the geese of one species tend to flock together. But geese of other species sometimes occur with them, and in fact the different species differ from each other in the colour of the beak and the wing-pattern, which perhaps serve as recognition marks.

In the shelducks in the genus *Tadorna*, unlike most other waterfowl, the nest is concealed in a hole, so there is much less need for the female to have concealing colouring, and in fact she has bright and distinctive plumage, like the male. However, there are other hole-nesting ducks, such as the goldeneyes *Bucephala* and the Wood Duck *Aix sponsa*, in which the female is much duller than the male.

Parallels to these findings occur in other birds. For instance, in various other hole-nesting species, such as bee-eaters and woodpeckers, the female is brightly coloured like the male. In contrast, in many song-birds with cup-shaped nests on the ground or in bushes, the need for concealing colouring is great, and since both sexes share in raising the brood, the males are as dully coloured as the females. But in songbirds each species has distinctive song, which presumably helps the female to select a male of her own species. Hence the male warbler's song probably has the same function as the drake Mallard's bright colours.

FIGURE 21. Display in northern dabbling ducks: Teal *Anas crecca* (a), Pintail *A. acuta* (b) and Mallard *A. platyrhynchos* (c); with Yellow-billed Duck *A. undulata* (d), a tropical dabbling duck in which the sexes look alike.

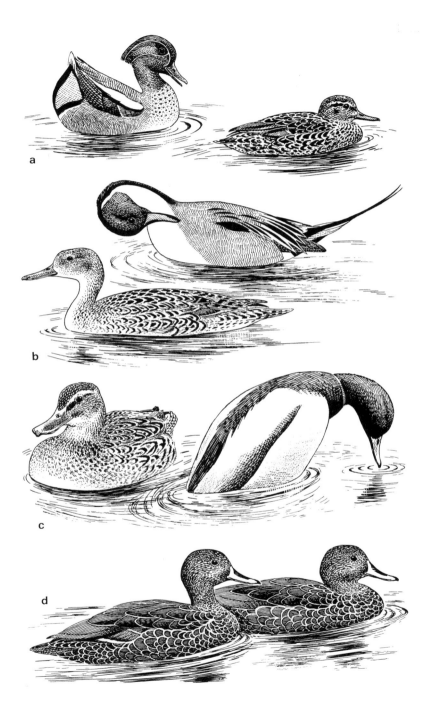

a

b

c

d

This discussion shows that the colouring of male birds has been evolved as a compromise between two conflicting advantages, that of conspicuousness to females seeking mates and that of inconspicuousness to predators. The same principle of compromise applies to many other parts of the body. For instance, waterfowl use their legs for both swimming and walking, but the most efficient position is near the middle of the body for walking but near the back for swimming, and the position evolved is a compromise, depending on the way of life of the species concerned.

17 · SEXUAL SELECTION

In his theory of *Sexual Selection*, published 12 years after the *Origin of Species*, Darwin attributed the bright colouring of the males of many animals to the females choosing the brighter in preference to the duller ones as mates. But since, in most birds, the sex ratio is nearly equal and each female mates with only one male, he realized that nearly every male would get a mate in the end, so that the brighter males would have no special advantage, except perhaps in being able to breed earlier than the others. Critics of his views also pointed out that there was no reason why all females of the same species should prefer the same pattern of bright colours in their mates. Hence while Darwin was correct in supposing that bright male plumage is advantageous in mating, he did not find the right reasons for it.

Waterfowl have bizarre displays (Fig. 22), and many of the males have evolved elongated feathers or bright colours which accentuate their postures. For instance, if the male has a crest, like the drake Red-breasted Merganser *Mergus serrator*, one can be sure that the head will feature prominently in display, and

FIGURE 22. Display of Red-breasted Merganser *Mergus serrator* (a), Mandarin *Aix galericulata* (b) and King Eider *Somateria spectabilis* (c).

a

b

c

in fact the drake stretches out its long neck into a snake-like attitude and then jerks the head forward and back, at the same time raising and lowering the crest. Again, the Mandarin Duck *Aix galericulata* has greatly enlarged inner secondary feathers on the wing, which project up vertically, and it also expands its crest and the long chestnut feathers on the neck. The male King Eider *Somateria spectabilis* stretches the head forward and then throws it back rapidly, the movement being accentuated by its orange bill with enlarged knob and its blue-grey crown, and at the same time the bird utters a cooing note. Many other examples could be described, but neither a written description nor a still picture can convey the strangeness and often beauty of these performances; one needs to see them in life, or at least in a coloured ciné film.

The displays formerly classed loosely as 'courtship' have three different functions, which involve partly different movements. First, they help the male to attract a female to form a pair, and it is then, as discussed in the previous chapter, that it is important for the female to recognize males of her own species, which is why the males of each species are distinctive. Secondly, the male has threat displays, by which it drives off rival males. Thirdly, shortly before the eggs are laid, often several weeks after the pair has been formed, the male displays to the female to bring her into the physiological and psychological condition in which she is ready to copulate. The function of all these displays is to attract attention and communicate with other individuals. They are a sign language and it is essential that each sign should be correctly recognised by the bird for which it is intended.

In at least some species of geese and swans, a male and female stay paired until one of them dies. The male helps the female in escorting the young, and since young swans have too short necks to pull up weeds from the bottom of the water, the adults pull it up for them. Further, the young stay with their parents after fledging and travel with them to the traditional wintering grounds of the species, and thus learn where these are situated.

There is one further advantage of life-pairing, since it has been shown in certain other kinds of birds that breeding starts earlier if the two members of the pair know each other from a previous year than if they are strangers. This may be particularly important for swans and geese, as most of them nest in the arctic, where the young have to complete their development before the end of the short summer, so breeding starts as soon as it is possible.

FIGURE 23. Pair of Musk Ducks *Biziura lobata*; note larger male.

Most other waterfowl, like the majority of other birds, are monogamous in the sense that a male mates with only one female for a season, but after breeding they separate, and each may have a different mate in a later year. In most birds, the main advantage of monogamy is that both parents help to feed the young, but though swans and also whistling ducks pull up food for their young, the young of nearly all other waterfowl find food for themselves from hatching. Moreover in many ducks the male deserts the female just after the eggs have been laid. The advantage to them of monogamy is not clear.

A few waterfowl, such as the Muscovy Duck *Cairina moschata* and the Australian Musk Duck *Biziura lobata*, have no definite pair bond but are promiscuous, each male seeking to copulate with several females. In such species, there must be unusually strong selection for those characters which make for success in mating, because successful males have several females in a season, while others have none. The male pursues the female over the water so strength may be one important attribute, and this is probably why the male Muscovy and Musk Ducks, unlike those of other waterfowl, are about twice as heavy as the females (Fig. 23). The size of the female has presumably been evolved in relation to the feeding habits of the species, and the feeding habits probably impose an upper limit on the size to which the male can successfully evolve. More often in birds, promiscuity is linked with brilliant colouring and extravagant adornments in the males, as in various birds of paradise. Here also, a counteracting disadvantage prevents too extreme a development, since the more heavily adorned males are more likely to be caught by predators. As in other cases, the end result is a compromise, the males continuing to evolve more brilliant plumage so long as the resulting increase in the average number of their offspring more than offsets their increased risk of being killed by enemies.

Clearly, 'sexual selection' is more complex than Darwin stated, and female 'choice' plays a very minor part. It is therefore better not to speak of sexual selection, but of the functions of the secondary sexual characters of birds, and to regard these characters as a result of natural selection, through the usual compromise between counteracting advantages and disadvantages.

18 · COMPETITION BETWEEN SPECIES

If two forms, originally subspecies of one species, later meet in the same area and do not interbreed, they have become full species, but they will then be in potential competition, and the chance is negligible that they will be equally well adapted. Either, one is generally less efficient than the other and is eliminated, or each prove better adapted to certain types of the available habitats or foods, in which case they can co-exist. Ecological isolation is just as essential for their continued existence in the same area as is the sexual isolation previously discussed. As mentioned in Chapter 12, it is wrong to suppose that new species of birds arise from populations living in the same area but in different habitats. That, nevertheless, related species often occupy separate habitats is because they could not persist in the same area unless they did so; this is a result, not a cause, of the formation of new species. Hence when two species meet in the same area, any ecological differences between them will tend to become intensified by natural selection. This is the principle of 'competitive exclusion' (formerly called 'Gause's principle').

Three main types of isolation are found in closely related species of birds: (i) they may have similar ecology but live in separate areas, (ii) they may feed on similar types of food but in separate habitats, and (iii) they may live in the same habitat but on different types of food. The first of these is the simplest. For example, three kinds of grey goose graze commonly on grass pastures in Britain in winter, the European Whitefront *Anser a. albifrons* chiefly in the Severn valley and mid-Wales, the Greenland Whitefront *A. albifrons flavirostris* chiefly in Ireland and parts of western Scotland, and the Greylag *A. anser* chiefly in eastern, with some in southwest, Scotland. Hence they scarcely overlap in range with each other.

Other geese found in Britain in winter are isolated mainly by habitat. The Whitefront, just mentioned, feeds on inland pastures, the Pink-footed Goose *Anser (f.) brachyrhynchus* chiefly on arable land, the Barnacle Goose *Branta leucopsis* on spray-blown Atlantic islands and grass on saltmarshes, and the Brent Goose *Branta bernicla* on estuarine mudflats at low tide (Fig. 24).

Differences in diet among species living in the same habitat are harder to determine, but a good example is provided by five species of dabbling ducks studied in the Medway estuary in Kent in winter (Fig. 25). Of these, the Wigeon *Anas penelope* plucks grass above high watermark and also takes saltwater green algae. The Shoveler *Anas clypeata* strains micro-organisms through its beak from the surface of the water, though it also takes larger items. The Pintail *Anas acuta* up-ends for plants on the bottom to a greater depth than the others and also feeds more than the rest in the intertidal zone. The Mallard *Anas platyrhynchos*, which is the largest species, feeds more than the rest in brackish ditches, while it and the Pintail are the only two which often grub in the mud, and it and the Teal *Anas crecca*, which is much the smallest species, are the only two which take many seeds. Correlated with these differences, the Wigeon has a short beak, high at the base, and strong jaws, which are adapted for pulling off leaves. The Shoveler has narrow ridges or lamellae on the sides of the beak forming a fine strainer. The Pintail has a longer neck than the others. The Teal is so small that it cannot reach so deep as the others when up-ending, but can probably pick up smaller organisms, and the lamellae on its beak are closer together than in the Mallard or Pintail. Hence of these five species the Wigeon takes almost completely different foods from the rest, and though the other four have some abundant foods in common, each differs in important respects from the others.

To complete the picture, two ducks in other genera also feed

FIGURE 24. Geese feeding in winter: Brent *Branta bernicla* (a), Barnacle *B. leucopsis* (b), White-fronted *Anser albifrons* (c) and Pink-footed *A. (f.) brachyrhynchos* (d).

a

b

c

d

in the Medway estuary, and while five dabbling ducks eat primarily plant matter, the Goldeneye *Bucephala clangula* dives in the deeper channels for crustacea and the Shelduck *T. tadorna* picks up small molluscs *Hydrobia ulvae* from the intertidal zone (which are also taken when abundant by the dabbling ducks).

A similar degree of ecological isolation has been found among the ducks in an Australian swamp, where the Wood Duck *Chenonetta jubata* feeds on grass pastures, the Grey Teal *Anas gibberifrons* on grass, smartweed and small insects, the Black Duck *Anas superciliosa* on the same plants and larger insects, the Blue-billed Duck *Oxyura australis* on sedges and midge larvae, the Hardhead *Aythya australis* on large insects and large molluscs obtained by diving, the Musk Duck *Biziura lobata*, which dives deeper, on crayfish, large mussels and deepwater weeds, the Pink-eared Duck *Malacorhynchus membranaceus* on minute particles filtered from the surface, and the Freckled Duck *Stictonetta naevosa* on algae filtered from shallow water. (I have here used the Australian vernacular names; see Appendix 1 for the English ones.) Clearer evidence for differences in diet has been found in various types of birds in which, under natural conditions, each species depends on different kinds or sizes of prey, or on prey caught by different methods or in different parts of the habitat.

Although the ecological isolation of each species is due to competition, such competition is rarely seen. For one thing, it is not usually direct, in the sense of one species driving another away. Instead, if a species seeks to live in a habitat to which it is less well adapted than other species, it or its young have a smaller chance of survival, so it soon dies out there. Further, if it survives better in one habitat than another, it will usually evolve behaviour to recognize it, hence birds rarely settle in an unfavourable habitat. This behaviour is called 'habitat selection', but it would disappear unless reinforced by periodic failures in

· FIGURE 25. Dabbling ducks feeding: Shoveler *Anas clypeata* (a), Mallard *A. platyrhynchos* (b), Pintail *A. acuta* (c), Teal *A. crecca* (d) and Wigeon *A. penelope* (e).

a

b

c

d

e

unfavourable habitats. Similarly, each species learns to avoid seeking for foods which it cannot obtain in sufficient quantities in competition with other species. But if a type of food is temporarily so plentiful that there is no real competition for it, then several species may take it. The places where a species feeds within its habitat are called its 'ecological niche'.

19 · ADAPTIVE RADIATION

As discussed in the previous chapter, if two species are to persist in the same area, they must evolve ecological differences. Since closely related species tend to have similar adaptations, these differences will at first be simple, for instance in habitat rather than diet. But with time, bigger differences and more complex adaptations are likely to be evolved, while further new species may spread into the area, each of which, if it is to persist, must likewise evolve ecological differences, leading to further specialisation in habitat or diet and resulting adaptations.

When a group of animals has evolved many diverse species with different feeding adaptations, it is termed an 'adaptive radiation'. A classical instance is that of the marsupial or pouched mammals of Australasia, which include plant-eaters, insect-eaters and flesh-eaters, runners, tree-climbers, burrowers and aerial gliders. But the waterfowl provide a similar, though less spectacular, example. A first look at them in the Wildfowl Trust collection might suggest that all are very similar, but they are not here seen hunting for food in their natural surroundings. In fact the waterfowl are very diverse. In western Europe or North America, for instance, ten types of feeding occur (some of which were already mentioned in the previous chapter) (Fig. 26):

FIGURE 26. Australian waterfowl feeding: Australian White-eye *Aythya australis* (a), Musk Duck *Biziura lobata* (b), Blue-billed Duck *Oxyura australis* (c), Black Duck *Anas superciliosa* (d), Freckled Duck *Stictonetta naevosa* (e), Grey Teal *A. gibberifrons* (f) and Pink-eared Duck *O. australis* (g).

1   Most dabbling ducks in the genus *Anas* feed on plant matter, both by up-ending in shallow water to reach the bottom, and by dabbling along the surface with rapid movements of the beak, using the lamellae of the beak as a coarse filter.

2   Swans *Cygnus* also feeds on plants by up-ending, but they reach far deeper, as they have extremely long necks.

3   The Shoveler *Anas clypeata* also dabbles, but for much finer particles. It swims with the beak half-submerged and partly open, drawing in water through the unusually broad tip and expelling it through the fine lamellae, from which the sensitive tongue removes micro-organisms. 'Filter-feeding', also found in flamingos and whalebone whales, is an adaptation enabling an animal to subsist on creatures far smaller than itself, provided that they are abundant.

4   The Shelduck *T. tadorna* specialises on small saltwater molluscs in the intertidal zone, and has an unusually small beak for its size.

5   Most pochards *Aythya* feed mainly on vegetable matter by diving to the bottom of shallow lakes; they dabble at times.

6   Most sea ducks, such as eiders *Somateria* and scoters *Melanitta*, dive deeper than pochards, and eat mainly shellfish, also crustacea.

7   One sea duck, the Harlequin *H. histrionicus*, likewise feeds on marine molluscs in winter, but in summer takes insect larvae and crustacea from under stones in rushing streams.

8   One other group of sea ducks, the mergansers *Mergus*, catch fish by swimming under water, and their thin hooked beaks have tooth-like serrations pointing backward to hold their slippery prey.

9   Many geese in the genus *Anser* graze on grass, cutting it off by a scissors-like action of the sharp edges of the lower mandible against the blunt edges of the upper one. Some of them eat long grass and have long beaks, like the Bean Goose *Anser fabalis*, while others eat short grass and have short beaks, like Ross's Goose *Anser rossi*.

10   The Snow Goose *Anser caerulescens* grubs for tubers and

rhizomes and has a shorter and thicker beak than the grazing species. (Note that, of these groups, the Harlequin, the Snow Goose and Ross's Goose do not normally occur in Britain, and the Shelduck and Bean Goose do not occur in North America.)

This adaptive radiation of the northern waterfowl is the more striking in that they are all built on a common plan, partly due to their common ancestry and partly to their need to swim and fly efficiently. Their chief anatomical differences are in the beak, already mentioned, but they have others. For instance, eiders have an unusually strong gizzard for grinding up mollusc shells, and the intestine of the Shoveler is unusually long for absorbing nourishment from a 'soup' of micro-organisms mixed with inedible matter. Again, mergansers swim fast under water, so have the feet at the back of the body, which makes them clumsy on land, while geese walk for their food so have the feet in the middle of the body, which means that they cannot swim so fast.

Most of the different types of feeding mentioned in this chapter, and their associated adaptations, are characteristic of all the species in a genus. As discussed in Chapter 4, the genus is an arbitrary unit of classification. Nevertheless modern workers on the waterfowl agree fairly well as to which species should be put in each genus, so there are evidently natural gaps between them. These have probably arisen because each genus is, so to speak, a successful 'model' adapted to a particular way of life. Once a new model has been evolved, it is likely to spread into different areas and habitats, and to give rise to several species, while forms intermediate between this and another model may be less efficient than either and become extinct. Similarly at a higher taxonomic level, the first kind of waterfowl to appear in the world was evidently a successful new model for a freshwater bird, and later spread and became divided into many different species, probably eliminating aquatic birds of other families in the process, so that at the present day the species in the family Anatidae are clearly separated from those in other families.

20 · CONVERGENT EVOLUTION

When a group of animals has an adaptive radiation in one part of the world, and a different group has one in another region, species from each group may evolve a similar way of life and similar adaptations so that they come to look rather alike. For instance, the Australasian pouched mammals include a marsupial wolf and a marsupial mole, so called because in habits and anatomy they resemble the unrelated Old World wolf and mole respectively. The evolution of similar adaptations in unrelated animals is called 'convergent evolution' because,

FIGURE 27. Goosander *Mergus merganser* (a), Shag *Phalacrocorax aristotelis* (b), Torrent Duck *Merganetta armata* (c) and Finfoot *Heliornis fulica* (d).

68

though their respective ancestors were very different, they have 'converged' in appearance.

Good examples occur in waterfowl. As mentioned in the previous chapter, the mergansers *Mergus* are adapted to catch fish by swimming under water. So are cormorants *Phalacrocorax*, and the illustration (Fig. 27) shows how alike these two genera are. Both have webbed feet set far back on the body, so that they swim fast under water but walk clumsily on land, both have streamlined bodies, and both have long necks and thin hooked beaks for catching their prey. Indeed cormorants are sometimes mistaken for ducks by inexperienced bird-watchers. It might therefore be asked why they are not put in the same family. The answer is that their resemblances are superficial. Mergansers resemble other ducks in their internal anatomy, their courtship displays, and in having active downy young which leave the nest and feed for themselves from hatching. Cormorants, on the other hand, resemble gannets and pelicans in their internal anatomy, and in having helpless naked young which stay in the nest and are fed entirely by their parents until they can fly. Hence they are classified in a different family, the Phalacrocoracidae, and a different order, the Pelecaniformes, from the order Anseriformes which includes the waterfowl.

Another good example, this time from South America, concerns the Torrent Duck *Merganetta armata* and the finfoot *Heliornis fulica*, both of which are adapted for swimming in fast-flowing rivers. But again, their marked similarities are superficial. The Torrent Duck is clearly one of the Anatidae, while the finfoots are put in a family of their own, the Heliornithidae, in the order Gruiformes, which also includes the rails Rallidae.

These examples refer to species in different orders of birds, but convergent evolution also occurs between species in different tribes of the same family in waterfowl. For instance the geese of the Northern Hemisphere in the genus *Anser*, which are in the tribe Anserini and the subfamily Anserinae, look very like the sheldgeese of the Southern Hemisphere in the genus *Chloe-*

phaga, which are in the tribe Tadornini and the subfamily Anatinae. Both these genera are adapted for grazing, they have

FIGURE 28. Convergent evolution for grazing between a typical goose (Emperor) (a), a South American Sheldgoose (Andean) (b) and the Australian Maned Goose (c).

similar beaks (Fig. 28) with a sharp cutting lower mandible, and legs similarly placed near the middle of the body. Indeed they were for a long time classified together, but the evidence from internal anatomy, colour of plumage and behaviour has shown this to be wrong. Another unrelated species, but with similar grazing habits and beak structure, is the Maned Goose or Australian Wood Duck *Chenonetta jubata*, which is in yet another different tribe, the Cairinini. As grass is widespread, one would expect to find grazing waterfowl in different regions of the world, and it is presumably due to the historical factor of which types were present in earlier times, that the birds filling this ecological niche in, respectively, high northern latitudes, southern South America and Australia, are of different origin. Another grazing waterfowl, again of different origin, is the Wigeon *Anas penelope*, one of the dabbling ducks, but it is less extreme and could hardly be thought of as a goose.

FIGURE 29. Heads of Shoveler *Anas clypeata* (left) and Pink-eared Duck *Malacorhynchus membranaceus* (right).

Convergence may also occur between two genera in the same tribe. The filter-feeding habits and adaptations of the Northern Shoveler *Anas clypeata* were described in the previous shapter, and similar-looking species in South America, South Africa and Australasia are probably of common origin, as they have similar colour patterns. But also in Australia occurs the Pink-eared Duck *Malacorhynchus membranaceus*, which has similar feeding habits and a somewhat similar beak to the Shoveler (Fig. 29) but looks very different in other ways, and is agreed to be of independent origin, though in the same tribe Anatini. Compared with the true shovelers, its beak is longer, with more numerous lamellae and with overlapping flaps on the upper beak, so that it forms a more efficient filter, and it holds the beak deeper in the water, at times feeding along the muddy bottom. At times, also, two birds rotate in small circles, each filtering in the wake of the other. Their main food consists of algae. The ducklings feed similarly to the adults and have a similar beak,

71

whereas shoveler ducklings feed like those of other dabbling ducks and develop the specialised beak later in life.

Another probable example of convergence in waterfowl is between the northern eiders *Somateria* and the South American steamer-ducks *Tachyeres*, both of which dive for molluscs on the sea bottom and are large heavy birds with similar beaks, and feet near the back of the body. But the classification of both groups is uncertain, though it is agreed that they are not closely related.

FIGURE 30. Heads of Lesser Whitefront *Anser erythropus* (a), Ross's Goose *A. rossi* (b), Cackling Goose *Branta canadensis minima* (c) and Red-breasted Goose *B. ruficollis* (d).

Convergent resemblances can occur at every taxonomic level. For instance, hummingbirds and hawkmoths, both adapted for sucking nectar from flowers while hovering, are in different phyla, while penguins and porpoises, both adapted for swimming, are in different classes of animals. At the other end of the scale, convergence may occur even between species in the same genus. For instance, four kinds of northern geese eat very short grass and have very short beaks (Fig. 30), but none of them are very closely related to each other. Two of them are in the genus *Anser*, namely the Lesser Whitefront *A. erythropus*, which is most nearly related to the Whitefront *A. albifrons*, and Ross's Goose *A. rossi*, which is most nearly related to the Snow Goose *A. caerulescens*. The other two are in the same genus *Branta*, namely the Cackling Goose *B. canadensis minima*, which is the smallest race of the Canada Goose, and the Red-breasted Goose *B. ruficollis*, whose nearest relative is uncertain but it is not the Canada Goose. In both genera, therefore, the resemblances in beak are due to convergence. (The Lesser White-front and Red-breasted Goose live in the Old World and Ross's and the Cackling Goose in the New World.)

21 · ADAPTATIONS FOR BREEDING

The adaptations so far considered play a part in the origin of species, either through preventing interbreeding or through reducing competition for food. Waterfowl have many other adaptations, in antomy, physiology and behaviour, and some of those which interest the field naturalist will be mentioned in this and the following chapter.

We often take it for granted that birds lay their eggs only at those seasons when they can raise young. But this involves complex timing, for the sex organs start to develop well before the eggs are laid. Two types of factors are involved. The 'ultimate factors' are those concerned with the evolution, through natural selection, of a particular breeding season, with the advantages of breeding then rather than at some other time. In the arctic, for instance, only those geese which lay eggs at the

73

start of the short summer have time to raise fledged young. To do this, some species arrive on the breeding grounds with eggs ready to lay, presumably having copulated before setting out on the last stage of their northward journey.

FIGURE 31. Dabbling duck female with cryptic colouring sitting tight as predator approaches.

The 'proximate factors' are those which affect the bird's physiology and behaviour so that it forms and lays its eggs at the most suitable season; they are timing factors. For instance, in the Mallard *Anas p. platyrhynchos* and other northern birds, the growth of the male sex organs is stimulated by increasing daylength in spring, and if captive birds are given artificial lighting after nightfall in winter, they develop their sex organs unusually early. Increased daylength does not have any basic effect on the sex organs, it is simply a signal, which travels from the eye to the brain, from the brain to the pituitary gland under the brain, and from there through the blood to the sex organs. Since different northern species breed at rather different

74

times, they respond to this signal rather differently. In the tropics, there is no appreciable change in daylength during the year, and here different proximate factors may be used.

FIGURE 32. Nest, eggs and lining of down.

Most waterfowl nest amid vegetation in a hollow in the ground. Concealing colouring would be little help for such large and numerous eggs, and instead the female has concealing colouring and sits closely (Fig. 31). Further, she lines the nest with down from her body, and if she leaves, she pulls this over the eggs, which helps to conceal them (Fig. 32); the down also helps to keep the eggs warm, hence its commercial use in eider-down. In addition, if the female is flushed by an enemy, she may flutter over the ground or the water as if she cannot fly, which often draws the enemy away from her eggs or young. Further, waterfowl often nest on small islands, which protects them from many ground mammals, while in Scandinavia, the Tufted Duck *Aythya fuligula* and the Eider *Somateria mollissima* get protection by nesting in gull colonies, as the gulls drive off many egg-thieves such as crows. Some other ducks nest safely in holes, but such sites are sparse.

75

Each kind of waterfowl lays a clutch of characteristic size, ranging from two in the Musk Duck *Biziura lobata* to 10 or more in certain dabbling and diving ducks. Each species also lays eggs of characteristic size, ranging from 2·5 per cent of the body-weight in the White-winged Wood Duck *Cairina scutulata* to 15 per cent or more of the body-weight in some of the stifftails *Oxyura*. In general, the species with larger clutches have relatively smaller eggs, and conversely, which suggests that clutch-size has been evolved in relation to the size of the eggs and of the female's food reserves. On this view, there must be some advantage in a larger egg sufficient, in the species concerned, to outweigh the disadvantage of a smaller clutch. Larger eggs give rise to larger chicks, and the latter are perhaps advantageous in species in which the food supply at hatching is poor. But these views are speculative.

It used at one time to be supposed that young animals, in their development, pass through ('recapitulate') the evolutionary stages of their ancestors. But this is misleading, and ignores the fact that the young are adapted to their own way of life. Ducklings, for instance, hatch with disproportionately large feet and tiny wings, not because their ancestors looked like this, but because they escape from their enemies by swimming, not flying. For the same reason, the growth of their flight feathers is greatly retarded, and they cannot fly until after they are fully grown in other respects. Hence sportsmen call them 'flappers', a word also used in the nineteen-twenties for girls who were just grown-up. In contrast to ducklings, the downy chicks of game-birds like the Pheasant *Phasianus colchicus* have grown short wings and can fly a few yards when only a few days old. This likewise has nothing to do with their ancestors, but a flight of a few yards is enough to take a chick away from a prowling fox, and when it lands, it crouches motionless. Likewise a duckling, after swimming under cover, stays still in the water. Both kinds of young are then helped by their cryptic (concealing) colouring, which is another important adaptation.

Feathers, like clothing, wear out and have to be renewed, which is usually done by a complete moult after breeding. In most birds, only one or two of the flight feathers are renewed at one time, so that flight is not seriously impaired, but waterfowl shed all the quills together, which has the advantage of a rapid moult,

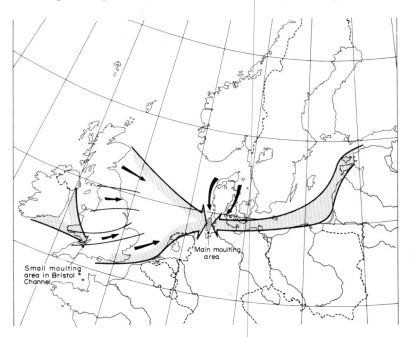

FIGURE 33. Map of moult migration of Shelduck.

but the disadvantage that the birds become temporarily flightless. However, they do not catch their food on the wing, and being on the water, they are fairly safe from enemies. Further, as mentioned in Chapter 16, the brightly coloured males of many ducks moult temporarily into a cryptic 'eclipse' plumage until they can fly again.

As a further protection, various species travel to moult in unusually safe areas with abundant food. For instance, adult Shelducks *Tadorna tadorna* move in late summer from England

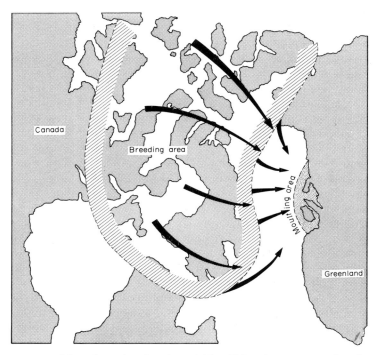

FIGURE 34. Map of moult migration of King Eider, from eastern Canada to the west coast of Greenland.

to the sands of the Heligoland Bight, returning after completing their moult (Fig. 33). Similarly, male and sub-adult King Eiders *Somateria spectabilis* travel from Canada to the west coast of Greenland (Fig. 34), immature geese of several species move to snow-free land in the far north, and various northern dabbling ducks travel to remote mountain lakes in Central Asia (Fig. 35).

Such 'moult migrations' are a speciality of waterfowl. In

addition, the northern species migrate in the normal way for birds from breeding areas where they could not survive the winter to milder areas, hundreds or even thousands of miles distant. For instance, the Garganey *Anas querquedula* travels from Europe southward to tropical Africa (Fig. 36), while various geese and ducks breeding in arctic U.S.S.R. move west and a little south to the British Isles. The advantage of seeking a warm wintering area is clear, but the advantage of leaving it again in spring is less obvious. However, if the birds concerned did not do so, their present breeding grounds would stand empty, and probably they can raise more young there than if they stayed in their winter quarters.

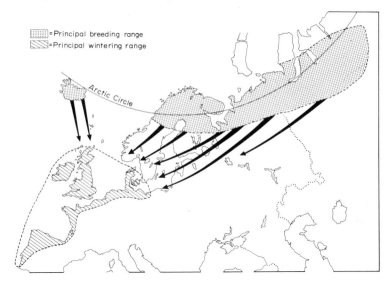

FIGURE 35. Map of migration of Wigeon.

As mentioned in Chapter 17, young geese and swans learn the position of their wintering grounds by migrating with their parents. But young ducks do not travel with their parents, so how do they know where to go? It has been shown that ducks, like various other birds, can travel on a fixed course with the

79

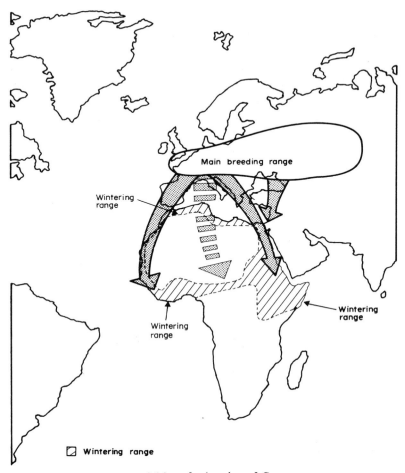

Main breeding range

Wintering range

Wintering range

Wintering range

Wintering range

FIGURE 36. Map of migration of Garganey.

help of the sun's bearing. To do this, they must allow for the changing position of the sun in the course of the day. That they have some sort of 'clock' has been shown by experiments in which captive ducks were kept for a number of days in a darkened room in which electric lighting was regularly turned on and off several hours out of phase with the real day and night. When such birds were released outside, they flew off in the wrong direction, because the position of the sun in relation to their shifted time of day gave them a wrong bearing (which varied proportionately to the amount by which their time of day had been shifted). Probably, ducks inherit a sense of the direction which they should take on their autumn migration, and keep to it by using the sun by day and the stars by night. But whether they can compensate if drifted off-course by the wind, and how they know when they have reached the wintering-grounds, are unsolved problems.

In the semi-arid interior of Australia, rain comes irregularly, and an area may have temporary lakes in one season, and then none for several years. It would be useless for the ducks of such areas to migrate regularly between fixed breeding and fixed wintering grounds. Instead, they wander irregularly, settling to breed where they find water. Nomadism of this type is found in other birds in the same region, and also in the birds of other areas which have irregular food supplies.

Hence waterfowl have evolved several different types of movements, which enable them to take advantage of areas that provide their needs for only part of the year. Such long-distance movements are possible only because they have evolved the power of sustained flight. As a result they are not forced, like many other animals, to live dormant during the cold of winter or summer drought.

23 · CONCLUSION

The importance to Darwin's thinking of the finches which he found in the Galapagos Islands was that they provided, in that miniature world, a model of evolution. The waterfowl likewise provide a model of evolution, but in their case it is necessary to choose examples from many different regions. The chief aim of this book has been to demonstrate the successive stages from simple mutations to an adaptive radiation. But in the course of it various points were elaborated, and various side issues were discussed, so in conclusion it may be worth summarising the main theme.

The raw material of evolution consists of hereditary mutations which are inherited in such a way that they are not merged or swamped by cross-breeding. Each hereditary unit, or gene, has many effects and each part of the body is affected by many genes. Natural selection tends to preserve those combinations of genes in which the harmful effects of mutations are reduced and any beneficial effects are increased.

Geographical isolation is the essential first stage in the evolution of hereditary differences between bird populations. The differences between geographically isolated populations range from barely detectable differences in average measurement to differences as great as those which separate related species. Moreover in birds, as in other vertebrate animals, the only known half-way stage to a new species is a geographical race, or subspecies. It is therefore concluded that new species arise from geographical races which have become so distinct that, if they later meet in the same area, they do not normally interbreed. If, in isolation, such geographical forms have accumulated many hereditary differences, it is unlikely that their respective genes will combine well in hybrids between them. Hence when they meet in the same area, selection will favour those individuals which mate with members of their own, rather than the other, kind, and they will tend to evolve features and behaviour which help them to do this. In many waterfowl, one factor reducing interbreeding is the possession of distinctive male plumage.

If two forms meet in the same area and do not interbreed, thus becoming full species, it is essential, if one is not to eliminate the other, that they should not compete for food or other basic requirements. Hence any ecological differences between them when they meet are likely to become intensified with time, until they are effectively isolated from each other. Once ecological isolation had been evolved, each species may spread through

82

the range of the other, giving rise to further geographical races, some of which with other new species, may later meet in the same area and keep distinct. This process leads to an increasing subdivision of the ecological niches, and a corresponding increase in the specialised adaptations of each species, and eventually, under favourable conditions, to an adaptive radiation. Some of the species concerned in such a radiation may, through convergence, evolve similar adaptations to species in other groups which have adopted a similar way of life in another region.

APPENDIX 1 · LIST OF WATERFOWL
after Johnsgaard (1965)

Tribe Anseranatini
  Anseranas semipalmata Australian Magpie Goose

Tribe Dendrocygnini   Whistling or Tree Ducks
  Dendrocygna guttata Spotted Whistling Duck
  D. eytoni Plumed Whistling Duck or Grass Whistle-Duck
  D. bicolor Fulvous Whistling Duck
  D. arcuata Wandering Whistling Duck or Water Whistle-Duck
    (3 subspecies)
  D. javanica Indian Whistling Duck
  D. viduata White-faced Whistling Duck
  D. arborea Cuban Whistling Duck
  D. autumnalis Red-billed Whistling Duck (2 subspecies)

Tribe Anserini   Swans and Geese
  Cygnus olor Mute Swan
  C. atratus Black Swan
  C. melanocoryphus Black-necked Swan
  C. cygnus Whooper and Trumpeter Swans (2 subspecies)
  C. columbianus Bewick's and Whistling Swans (3 subspecies)
  Coscoroba coscoroba Coscoroba Swan
  Anser cygnoides Swan Goose
  A. fabalis Bean Goose (6 subspecies, including Pink-footed Goose)
  A. albifrons White-fronted Goose (4 subspecies)
  A. erythropus Lesser White-fronted Goose
  A. anser Greylag Goose (2 subspecies)
  A. indicus Bar-headed Goose
  A. caerulescens Snow and Blue Goose (2 subspecies)
  A. rossi Ross's Goose
  A. canagicus Emperor Goose
  Branta sandvicensis Hawaiian Goose or Ne-Ne
  B. canadensis Canada Goose (12 subspecies)

84

Tribe Anserini *continued*
  B. leucopsis Barnacle Goose
  B. bernicla Brent Goose or Brant (4 subspecies)
  B. ruficollis Red-breasted Goose
  Cereopsis novae-hollandiae Cape Barren Goose

Tribe Tadornini   Sheldgeese and Shelducks
  Cyanochen cyanopterus Abyssinian Blue-winged Goose
  Chloëphaga melanoptera Andean Goose
  C. picta Magellan Goose (2 subspecies)
  C. hybrida Kelp Goose (2 subspecies)
  C. poliocephala Ashy-headed Goose
  C. rubidiceps Ruddy-headed Goose
  Neochen jubatus Orinoco Goose
  Alopochen aegyptiacus Egyptian Duck
  Tadorna ferruginea Ruddy Shelduck
  T. cana Cape Shelduck
  T. variegata Paradise Shelduck
  T. tadornoides Australian Shelduck or Mountain Duck
  T. cristata Crested Shelduck (extinct)
  T. tadorna Common Shelduck
  T. radjah Radjah Shelduck or Burdekin Duck (2 subspecies)
  Tachyeres patachonicus Flying Steamer Duck
  T. pteneres Magellanic Flightless Steamer Duck
  T. brachypterus Falkland Flightless Steamer Duck

Tribe Cairinini   Perching Ducks
  Plectropterus gambensis Spur-winged Goose (2 subspecies)
  Cairina moschata Muscovy Duck
  C. scutulata White-winged Wood Duck
  Sarkidiornis melanotos Comb Duck (2 subspecies)
  Pteronetta hartlaubi Hartlaub's Duck (2 subspecies)
  Nettapus pulchellus Green Pygmy Goose
  N. coromandelianus Indian or White Pygmy Goose or Cotton Teal
    (2 subspecies)
  N. auritus African Pygmy Goose
  Callonetta leucophrys Ringed Teal
  Aix sponsa Wood Duck
  A. galericulata Mandarin Duck

85

Tribe Cairinini *continued*
    Chenonetta jubata Australian Wood Duck
    Amazonetta brasiliensis Brazilian Teal (2 subspecies)

Tribe Anatini   Dabbling Ducks
    Hymenolaimus malacorhynchus Blue Duck
    Stictonetta naevosa Freckled Duck
    Merganetta armata Torrent Duck (6 subspecies)
    Anas waigiuensis Salvadori's Duck
    A. sparsa African Black Duck (3 subspecies)
    A. penelope European Wigeon
    A. americana American Wigeon
    A. sibilatrix Chiloe Wigeon
    A. falcata Falcated Duck
    A. strepera Gadwall (2 subspecies)
    A. formosa Baikal Teal
    A. crecca Common Teal (3 subspecies)
    A. flavirostris South American Teal (4 subspecies)
    A. capensis Cape Teal
    A. gibberifrons Grey Teal (4 subspecies)
    A. bernieri Madagascan Teal
    A. castanea Chestnut Teal (probably includes next)
    A. aucklandica Brown Teal (3 subspecies) (extremely close to, if
      not conspecific with, Chestnut Teal)
    A. platyrhynchos Mallard (7 subspecies, including Laysan Teal)
    A. rubripes American Black Duck
    A. melleri Meller's Duck
    A. undulata Yellow-billed Duck (2 subspecies)
    A. poecilorhyncha Spot-billed Duck including Australian Black
      Duck (6 subspecies)
    A. luzonica Philippine Duck
    A. specularis Bronze-winged Duck
    A. specularioides Crested Duck (2 subspecies)
    A. acuta Pintail (3 subspecies)
    A. georgica Yellow-billed Pintail (3 subspecies)
    A. bahamensis Bahama Pintail (3 subspecies)
    A. erythrorhyncha Red-billed Pintail
    A. versicolor Silver Teal (3 subspecies)
    A. punctata Hottentot Teal

Tribe Anatini *continued*
  A. querquedula Garganey
  A. discors Blue-winged Teal
  A. cyanoptera Cinnamon Teal (5 subspecies)
  A. platalea Red Shoveler
  A. smithi Cape Shoveler
  A. rhynchotis Australian Shoveler (2 subspecies)
  A. clypeata Common Shoveler
  Malacorhynchus membranaceus Pink-eared Duck
  Marmaronetta angustirostris Marbled Teal

Tribe Aythyini   Pochards
  Rhodonessa caryophyllacea Pink-eared Duck (extinct)
  Netta rufina Red-crested Pochard
  N. erythrophthalma Southern Pochard (2 subspecies)
  N. peposaca Rosy-bill
  Aythya vallisneria Canvasback
  A. ferina European Pochard
  A. americana Redhead
  A. collaris Ring-necked Duck
  A. australis Australian White-eye or Hardhead (2 subspecies)
  A. baeri Baer's Pochard
  A. nyroca Common White-eye or Ferruginous Duck
  A. innotata Madagascar White-eye
  A. novae-seelandiae New Zealand Scaup
  A. fuligula Tufted Duck
  A. marila (Greater) Scaup (2 subspecies)
  A. affinis Lesser Scaup

Tribe Mergini   Scoters, Goldeneyes and Mergansers
  Somateria mollissima Common Eider (5 subspecies)
  S. spectabilis King Eider
  S. fischeri Spectacled Eider
  Polysticta stelleri Steller's Eider
  Camptorhynchus labradorius Labrador Duck (extinct)
  Histrionicus histrionicus Harlequin Duck
  Melanitta nigra Common or Black Scoter (2 subspecies)
  Clangula hyemalis Long-tailed Duck
  M. perspicillata Surf Scoter

Tribe Mergini *continued*
   M. fusca Velvet or White-winged Scoter (4 subspecies)
   Bucephala albeola Bufflehead
   B. islandica Barrow's Goldeneye
   B. clangula Common Goldeneye (2 subspecies)
   Mergus cucullatus Hooded Merganser
   M. albellus Smew
   M. octosetaceus Brazilian Merganser
   M. serrator Red-breasted Merganser (2 subspecies)
   M. squamatus Chinese Merganser
   M. merganser Goosander (3 subspecies)
   M. australis Auckland Island Merganser (extinct)

Tribe Oxyurini   Stiff-tailed Ducks
   Heteronetta atricapilla Black-headed Duck
   Oxyura dominica Masked Duck
   O. jamaicensis Ruddy Duck (4 subspecies)
   O. leucocephala White-headed Duck
   O. maccoa Maccoa Duck
   O. vittata Argentine Ruddy Duck
   O. australis Australian Blue-billed Duck
   Biziura lobata Musk Duck
   Thalassornis leuconotus White-backed Duck (2 subspecies)

APPENDIX 2 · GLOSSARY OF BIOLOGICAL TERMS

adaptive radiation – the evolution of one group of birds into a diversity of ecological niches, with corresponding adaptations.

allopatric – living in different areas, hence allopatric speciation, the origin of new species from geographical races (*cf.* sympatric).

author's name – the name of the man who gave an animal its scientific name. It immediately follows the scientific name but is often omitted or abbreviated (to an initial letter if Linnaeus).

Bergmann's rule – forms of the same species of warm-blooded (homoiothermic) animals are larger in cold climates.

binomial nomenclature – the system invented by Linnaeus by which each species is referred to by two names, first the genus and then the species.

Cenozoic – geologically the most recent of the three great fossil-bearing periods, but lasting a much shorter time than the Palaeozoic or Mesozoic. It includes the Tertiary (Eocene, Oligocene, Miocene and Pliocene) and Quaternary (Pleistocene) and started 50–100 million years ago.

chromosomes – the microscopic structures in the centre of the cell which carry the hereditary units.

class – the unit of classification between the order and the phylum *e.g.* the birds form a class.

classification – the arrangement of living things, nowadays with related forms close together.

cline – gradual change, usually in the colour or size of a species, through part or the whole of its geographical range.

clutch – the number of eggs laid by a bird in its nest.

competition – two animals compete if they seek the same ecological requirement in the same area and there is not enough of it to go round, *e.g.* they often compete for food, but not for air (though air is just as essential for their existence).

competitive exclusion, principle of – the idea that, owing to competition, two species with the same ecological requirements cannot co-exist in the same area (formerly called Gause's principle).

convergent evolution – similar adaptations and appearance evolved by unrelated animals occupying similar ecological niches, normally in different regions.

copulation – the process by which the male introduces spermatozoa to fertilise the egg-cells of the female.

cryptic (of colouring) – concealing colouring.

dominant – a gene is dominant if its effects are shown in an organism even though it has received it from only one of its two parents (*cf.* recessive).

eclipse plumage – the dull concealing plumage into which many male ducks moult while flightless during the wing-moult.

ecological isolation – two species are ecologically isolated if they do not compete for essential requirements.

ecological niche – the particular part or parts of its habitat in which an animal lives or seeks its food, often used also with reference to its main foods.

endemic (referring to a species or subspecies) – peculiar to a particular area.

Eocene – part of the Tertiary and Cenozoic (*q.v.*).

family – a unit of animal classification above the genus and below the order *e.g.* the waterfowl Anatidae are a family. Families end in 'idae'.

filter-feeding – the straining process by which a large animal feeds on abundant organisms far smaller than itself.

Gause's principle – the principle of competitive exclusion (*q.v.*).

gene – the basic unit of heredity.

genetics – the science of heredity.

genotype – an organism with a particular collection of genes.

genus (adjective *generic*) – the unit of classification above the species. Generic names are started with a capital letter.

geographical race or subspecies – a population of a species occupying a restricted geographical area and differing genetically from populations of the same species elsewhere (see also seventy-five per cent rule).

gizzard – the part of a bird's stomach with strong muscular walls used for grinding the food.

Gloger's rule – forms of the same species are darker in damper climates.

habitat – the type of environment in which a species lives.

habitat selection – the behaviour by which a bird recognises the habitat of its species.

hybrid – the offspring of a union between parents of different species.

intestine – the lower part of the gut, where the nutritive elements in the food pass into the blood.

lamellae – ridges or serrations on the sides of the beak of various waterfowl.

micro-organisms – animals or plants so small that they are readily seen only through a microscope.

migration – the regular seasonal movements of animals from a breeding to a wintering area, and back again later (*cf.* nomadism).

mirror or speculum – the iridescent (*i.e.* shining) patch of colour on the wing of many ducks, especially dabbling ducks.

monogamy – a pair-bond between one male and one female (*cf.* polyandry where one female pairs with several males, and polygyny where one male pairs with several females; polygamy at times refers to both of these, and also to promiscuity (*q.v.*).

monotypic – the only one of its type in the next highest unit of classification, *e.g.* a monotypic species is the only species in its genus.

moult – the process by which a bird's feathers are renewed.

moult migration – the regular movement of a bird population to a special area to moult.

multiple hybrid – a hybrid whose ancestors include more than two species; it arises through the mating of hybrid birds of different parentage.

mutation – a hereditary change.

nail – the tip of the upper mandible on the beak of a waterfowl.

natural selection – term invented by Darwin for the means by which advantageous genetic differences come to replace disadvantageous ones under natural conditions. It is a far better term than either the 'struggle for existence' or the 'survival of the fittest', which are now obsolete.

nomadism – irregular movements of animals, usually in relation to irregular food supplies.

nomen conservandum – the scientific name of an animal which has been used for a long time but ought, on the strict rules of nomenclature, to be superseded by another, and which, to prevent confusion, has been declared valid by a special international committee of biologists.

order – a unit of classification between the family and the class. In birds, the names of the orders end in 'formes', as in Anseriformes.

'Origin of Species' – the title to which Darwin's book of 1859 is normally abbreviated.

pair formation – the process by which a male bird acquires a mate. In some species it occurs several weeks or even months before copulation.

phylum – the unit of classification below the Kingdom and above the class, *e.g.* the vertebrates form a phylum.

Pleistocene – the geological period starting about a million years ago, also called the Quaternary (see also next).

Pliocene – the most recent geological period in the Tertiary, starting about ten million years ago, and followed by the Pleistocene (Quaternary) (*q.v.*).

predator – natural enemy.

promiscuity – irregular mating and copulation without a definite pair bond.

proximate factors – the immediate physiological and psychological factors responsible, in particular, for the timing of different parts of the annual cycle, such as the breeding season (*cf.* ultimate factors).

Quaternary – see Pleistocene.

quill feathers – the main feathers of the wing used in flight (the primaries and secondaries).

recapitulation, theory of – the idea that an animal repeats in its development the evolutionary history of its ancestors (this view is seriously misleading).

recessive – a gene is recessive if its effects are shown only in organisms which have received it from both parents (*cf.* dominant).

secondary sexual characters – features found only in one of the two sexes, but omitting the sex organs. Used in birds especially for the ornamental feathers of males.

seventy-five per cent rule – a subspecies is recognised as valid if at least three-quarters of the specimens are distinguishable from those of other populations of the species.

sexual selection – Darwin's theory to account for the evolution of secondary sexual male characters through female choice.

speciation – the process by which new species are formed.

species (adjective *specific*) – two forms are different species if they differ hereditarily from each other in constant ways and do not normally interbreed in natural conditions.

speculum – see mirror.

subfamily – the unit of classification below the family. There are three subfamilies of waterfowl, the Anseranatinae, Anserinae and Anatinae. Subfamilies end in 'inae'.

subspecies – see geographical race.

sympatric – living in the same area, hence sympatric speciation, the supposed origin of new species from birds living in the same area but in different habitats.

syrinx – the vocal organ of a bird.

'Systema Naturae' – the catalogue of living organisms by Linnaeus, the 10th edition of which is used as the basis for present-day nomenclature.

taxonomy – the science of naming living organisms, or their classification.

Tertiary Period – see under Cenozoic.

threat display – display used between two birds, usually males of the same species, when fighting.

trinomial nomenclature – the use of a third subspecific name, in addition to the generic and specific names.

tribe – unit of classification between the genus and the subfamily, used in only a few families of birds, but these include the waterfowl.

type specimen – the specimen, kept in a museum, to which official description of a species or subspecies is attached.

typical race – the subspecies which bears the same subspecific name as the species (it need not be typical of the species in any other sense).

ultimate factors – the long-term evolutionary factors responsible for particular features, such as the breeding season, in contrast to the immediate physiological or psychological factors called proximate (*q.v.*). Ultimate factors are concerned with survival value, proximate factors with internal mechanisms (though mechanism is a bad term, as it suggests that an animal is a machine).

vernacular name – name (of a bird) in a popular language, in contrast to its scientific Latin name.

Wildfowl Trust – the organisation at Slimbridge, Gloucestershire, created by Peter Scott to support a collection of living waterfowl and research on the biology of waterfowl.

wild-type gene – a gene found in the wild type of an animal.

INDEX

Aix sponsa 52
  galericulata 23 (Fig. 9), 55 (Fig. 22), 56
Anas 16, 17, 19, 20, 50, 64
  acuta 9 (Fig. 1), 19, 21 (Fig. 8), 34, 53 (Fig. 21), 60, 63, (Fig. 25)
  americana 17
  aucklandica 37 (Fig. 15), 38
  a. aucklandica 37 (Fig. 15)
  a. chlorotis 37 (Fig. 15)
  bahamensis 34
  carolinensis 25, 26
  castanea 34, 37 (Fig. 15), 38
  chlorotis 38
  clypeata 9 (Fig. 1), 19, 21 (Fig 8), 23 (Fig. 9), 47, 60, 63 (Fig. 25), 66, 71, 71 (Fig. 29)
  crecca 9 (Fig. 1), 19, 21 (Fig. 8), 25, 26, 47, 53 (Fig. 21), 60, 63 (Fig. 25)
  c. crecca 26, 26 (Fig. 10)
  c. carolinensis 26, 26 (Fig. 10)
  cyanoptera 30
  georgica 34, 53 (Fig. 21)
  gibberifrons 62, 65 (Fig. 26)
  laysanensis 39
  leucophrys 20, 24
  oustaleti 50
  penelope 9 (Fig. 1), 19, 21 (Fig. 8), 60, 63 (Fig. 25), 71, 79 (Fig. 35)
  platyrhynchos 9 (Fig. 1), 16, 17, 19, 21 (Fig. 8), 28, 29 (Fig. 12), 30, 34, 35 (Fig. 14), 43 (Fig. 18), 45 (Fig. 19), 46, 50, 53 (Fig. 21), 60, 63 (Fig. 25), 74
    diazi 29
    fulvigula 29
    p. laysanensis 34, 35 (Fig. 14)
    p. platyrhynchos 28, 29 (Fig. 12), 35 (Fig. 14)
    p. wyvilliana 35 (Fig. 14)
  querquedula 21 (Fig. 8), 47, 79, 80 (Fig. 36)
  rubripes 18 (Fig. 6), 19
  specularioides 45 (Fig. 19)
  strepera 19, 21 (Fig. 8), 34, 47
  superciliosa 18 (Fig. 6), 34, 50, 65 (Fig. 26)
  undulata 53 (Fig. 21)
  wyvilliana 39
Anatidae 12, 25, 69
Anatinae 24, 70, 71
Anatini 22, 23 (Fig. 9), 24
Anatinidae 67
Anhimidae 25
Anser 22, 66, 69, 73
  albifrons 28, 28 (Fig. 11), 59, 60, 61 (Fig. 24). 73
  a. albifrons 28 (Fig. 11)
  a. flavirostris 28 (Fig. 11)

  anser 45 (Fig. 19), 46, 59
  brachyrhynchus 27, 38, 39 (Fig. 16), 60, 61 (Fig. 24)
  caerulescens 41, 42 (Fig. 17), 66, 73
  canagicus 70 (Fig. 28)
  cygnoides 45 (Fig. 19), 46
  erythropus 28, 28 (Fig. 11), 72 (Fig. 30), 73
  fabalis 27, 30, 38, 39 (Fig. 16), 66
  rossi 66, 72 (Fig. 30), 73
Anseranas semipalmata 22, 23 (Fig. 9)
Anseranatinae 22, 23 (Fig. 9)
Anseriformes 25, 69
Anserinae 22, 23 (Fig. 9), 24, 69, 70
Anserini 22, 23 (Fig. 9), 24, 69
Aves 25
Aythya 22, 66
  affinis 50
  americana 17
  australis 62, 65 (Fig. 26)
  collaris 47
  ferina 9 (Fig. 1), 47, 49 (Fig. 20), 50
  fuligula 9 (Fig. 1), 23 (Fig. 9), 49 (Fig. 20), 50, 76
Aythyini 23 (Fig. 9), 24

Baldpate 17
Bee-eater 52
Biziura lobata 57 (Fig. 23), 58, 62, 65 (Fig. 26), 76
Branta 22, 73
  bernicla 60, 61 (Fig. 24)
  canadensis 29, 30, 31, 32, 32 (Fig. 13), 38, 72 (Fig. 30), 73
  leucopsis 13 (Fig. 4), 60, 61 (Fig. 24)
  ruficollis 23 (Fig. 9), 72 (Fig. 30), 73
  sandvicensis 33, 38
Bucephala 52
  albeola 47
  clangula 10 (Fig. 2), 62

Cairina moschata 45 (Fig. 19), 46, 58
  scutulata 76
Cairinini 20, 23 (Fig. 9), 24, 70
Callonetta 20
  leucophrys 24
Carduelis carduelis 31
Cereopsis novae-hollandiae 14, 14 (Fig. 5), 20, 24
Charadrius hiaticula 33
Chaulelasmus 19
Chenonetta jubata 62, 70, 70 (Fig. 28)
Chloëphaga 22, 69
  melanoptera 70 (Fig. 28)
  picta 13 (Fig. 4)
Clangula hyemalis 18 (Fig. 7), 19, 20
Cormorant 8, 69
Crow 76

94

Cygnus 66
  cygnus buccinator 11 (Fig. 3)
  cygnus cygnus 9 (Fig. 1)
  columbianus 47
  olor 23 (Fig. 9)

Dafila 20
Dendrocygnini 22, 23 (Fig. 9)
Dendrocygna viduata 23 (Fig. 9)
Diver or loon 8
Dodo 36
Duck 34, 38, 47, 52, 76, 79, 80, 81
  Auckland Island 36, 38
  Aylesbury 45 (Fig. 19), 46
  Black (American) 18 (Fig. 6), 19
  Black (Australian) 18 (Fig. 6), 19, 62, 65 (Fig. 26)
  Blue-billed 62, 65 (Fig. 26)
  Bufflehead 47
  Crested 45 (Fig. 19), 46
  Dabbling or surface feeding 7, 19, 20, 24, 30, 31, 46, 50, 53 (Fig. 21), 60, 62, 63 (Fig. 25), 64, 71, 72, 74 (Fig. 31), 76, 78
  Diving 7, 24, 76
  Eider 24, 49 (Fig. 20), 66, 72
    Common 30, 76
    King 55 (Fig. 22), 56, 78, 78 (Fig. 34)
  Freckled 62, 65 (Fig. 26)
  Grey 34, 50
  Harlequin 66, 67
  Hawaiian 34, 35 (Fig. 14), 39
  Hybrid 47–50
  Indian Runner 46
  Khaki Campbell 45 (Fig. 19), 46
  Laysan 34, 35 (Fig. 14), 36, 38, 39, 41
  Long-tailed 18 (Fig. 7), 19, 20
  Muscovy 45 (Fig. 19), 46, 47, 58
  Musk 57 (Fig. 23), 58, 62, 65 (Fig. 26), 76
  Oustalet's 50
  Perching 20, 24
  Pink-eared 62, 65 (Fig. 26), 71, 71 (Fig. 29)
  Ring-necked 47
  Rouen 46
  Ruddy 23 (Fig. 9)
  Sea 7, 24, 66
  Stifftails 7, 24, 76
  Surface feeding see Dabbling ducks
  Torrent 30, 68 (Fig. 27), 69
  Tree or Whistling 7, 22, 23 (Fig. 9)
  Tufted 9 (Fig. 1), 23 (Fig. 9), 49 (Fig. 20), 50, 76
  Whistling or Tree 7, 22, 23 (Fig. 9)
  White-faced Whistling 23 (Fig. 9)
  White-winged Wood 76
  Wild see Mallard
  Wood or Australian Maned Goose 52, 62, 70, 70 (Fig. 28)
  Yellow-billed 53 (Fig. 21)

Eider See under Duck
Finch 34
  Darwin's 34, 81
Finfoot 68 (Fig. 27), 69
Flamingo 66

Gadwall 19, 21 (Fig. 8), 34, 35, 47
  Fanning Island 34, 36
Gannet 69
Garganey 21 (Fig. 8), 47, 79, 80 (Fig. 36)
Geese 7, 12, 15, 22, 30, 52, 56, 66, 67, 69, 73, 74, 78, 79
Goldeneye 10 (Fig. 2), 52, 62
Goldfinch (European) 31
Goosander 9 (Fig. 1), 68 (Fig. 27)
Goose Australian Maned 70, 70 (Fig. 28)
  Barnacle 13 (Fig. 4), 60, 61 (Fig. 24)
  Bean 27, 30, 38, 39 (Fig. 16), 66, 67
  Blue 41, 42 (Fig. 17), 44
  Brent or Brant 60, 61 (Fig. 24)
  Cackling 72 (Fig. 30), 73
  Canada 29, 30, 31, 32 (Fig. 13), 33, 38, 73
  Cape Barren 14, 14 (Fig. 5), 20, 24
  Chinese 45 (Fig. 19), 46
  Emperor 70 (Fig. 28)
  Farmyard 45 (Fig. 19)
  Greenland Whitefront 28 (Fig. 11), 59
  Greylag 45 (Fig. 19), 46, 47, 59
  Hawaiian 33, 38
  Lesser Snow 41, 42 (Fig. 17), 44
  Lesser Whitefronted 28, 28 (Fig. 11), 72 (Fig. 30), 73
  Magpie (Australian 22, 23 (Fig. 9), 24
  Pink-footed 27, 38, 39 (Fig. 16), 60, 61 (Fig. 24)
  Red-breasted 23 (Fig. 9), 72 (Fig. 30), 73
  Ross's 66, 67, 72 (Fig. 30), 73
  Snow 41, 44, 66, 67, 73
  Swan 45 (Fig. 19), 46
  Whitefronted 28, 28 (Fig. 11), 59, 60, 61 (Fig. 24), 73
Gruiformes 69
Gull 76
  Herring 40
  Lesser Black-backed 40

Hardhead 62
Hawkmoth 73
Hedyleptis 48
Heliornis fulica 68 (Fig. 27), 69
Heliornithidae 69
Histrionicus histrionicus 66 ·
Hummingbird 73
Hydrobia ulvae 62

Malacorhynchus membranaceus 62, 65 (Fig. 26). 71, 71 (Fig. 29)

Mallard 9 (Fig. 1), 16, 19, 21 (Fig. 8),
    28, 29, 29 (Fig. 12), 30, 34, 35, 36,
    39, 41, 43, 43 (Fig. 18), 45 (Fig.
    19), 46, 47, 49, 50, 52, 53 (Fig.
    21), 60, 63 (Fig. 25), 74
  Florida 29, 51
  Hawaiian See under Duck
  Laysan See under Duck
  Mexican 29, 51
  Northern 28, 35 (Fig. 14)
Mandarin 23 (Fig. 9), 55 (Fig. 22), 56
Mareca 19
Melanitta 66
Meleagris gallopavo 46
Merganetta armata 30, 68 (Fig. 27),
    69
Merganser 66, 67, 69
  Red-breasted 23 (Fig. 9), 54, 55
    (Fig. 22)
Mergini 23 (Fig. 9), 24
Mergus 66, 69
  albellus 9 (Fig. 1)
  merganser 9 (Fig. 1), 68 (Fig. 27)
  serrator 23 (Fig. 9), 54, 55 (Fig. 22)
Mocking-bird 34
Ne-ne or Hawaiian Goose 33, 34, 38
Netta 22
  erythrophthalma 49 (Fig. 20)
Nettapus ceromandelianus 11
    (Fig. 3)
Nettion 20

Old Squaw 19
Oxyura 76
  australis 62, 65 (Fig. 26)
  jamaicensis 23 (Fig. 9)
Oxyurini 23 (Fig. 9), 24

Passer domesticus 31
Parus major 40
  minor 40
Pelecaniformes 69
Pelican 69
Penguin 73
Phalacrocoracidae 69
Phalacrocorax 69
  aristotelis 68 (Fig. 27)
Phasianus colchicus 76
Pheasant 76
Pigeon 44
Pintail 9 (Fig. 1), 19, 21 (Fig. 8), 39, 53
    (Fig. 21), 60, 63 (Fig. 25)
  Bahama 34
  Chilean 34
  Kerguelen 34, 36, 39, 41
  Northern 34, 35, 36, 39, 41
Plover Ringed (European) 33
Pochard 9 (Fig. 1), 22, 24, 47, 49
    (Fig. 20), 50, 66
  American 17
porpoise 73

Querquedula 20

Rallidae 69

Raphus cucullatus 36
Redhead 17

Scaup Lesser 50
Scoter 66
Shag 68 (Fig. 27)
Sheldgoose Upland 13 (Fig. 4)
  South American 22, 24, 69, 70
    (Fig. 28)
Shelduck European 17, 20, 23 (Fig. 9),
    24, 49 (Fig. 20), 52, 62, 66, 67,
    77 (Fig. 33), 78
Shoveler 9 (Fig. 1), 19, 20, 21 (Fig. 8),
    23 (Fig. 9), 47, 60, 63 (Fig. 25),
    66, 67, 71, 71 (Fig. 29), 72
Skua Arctic 41
Smew 9 (Fig. 1)
Somateria 66, 72
  mollissima 30, 49 (Fig. 20), 76
  spectabilis 55 (Fig. 22), 56, 78, 78
    (Fig. 34)
Sparrow House 31
Spatula 20
Steamer-ducks 72
Stercorarius parasiticus 41
Stictonetta naevosa 62, 65 (Fig. 26)
Stifftails 24, 76
Swan 7, 12, 22, 24, 56, 66, 79
  Mute 23 (Fig. 9)
  Trumpeter 10, 11 (Fig. 3)
  Whistling 47
  Whooper 9 (Fig. 1)

Tachyeres 72
Tadorna 17, 20, 52
  tadorna 17, 23 (Fig. 9), 49 (Fig. 20),
    62, 66, 77 (Fig. 33), 78
Tadornini 23 (Fig. 9), 24, 70
Teal 9 (Fig. 1), 19, 21 (Fig. 8), 25, 26,
    26 (Fig. 10), 47, 53 (Fig. 21),
    60, 63 (Fig. 25)
  Brown 37 (Fig. 15), 38
  Chestnut 34, 36, 37 (Fig. 15), 38
  Chestnut (Auckland Island) 36,
    37 (Fig. 15), 38
  Cinnamon 30
  Cotton (or Pygmy Goose) 10, 11
    (Fig. 3)
  Green-winged (American) 25–26
    (Fig. 10)
  Grey 62, 65 (Fig. 26)
  Ringed (South American) 20, 24
Tit Great 40
Turkey Wild 46

Vertebrata 25

Warbler 52
White-eye (Australian) 65 (Fig. 26)
Wigeon European 9 (Fig. 1), 19, 21
    (Fig. 8), 60, 63 (Fig. 25), 71, 79
    (Fig. 35)
  American 17
Woodpecker 52

96